A Word in Season

A Word in Season

Dramatic dialogues for Special Sundays and other occasions

Paul S. Glass

Copyright © Paul S. Glass 2005

British Library Cataloguing in Publication data

A catalogue record for this book is available from the British Library

ISBN 1 85852 279 X

First published by Inspire
4 John Wesley Road
Werrington
Peterborough PE4 6ZP

Covers printed in Great Britain by
Peterborough Printing Services

Dedication

To Janet – it would not have been possible without you.

Acknowledgements

A huge debt of thanks to my wife Janet for listening, caring and coping. Thanks also to Natalie Watson from Inspire for her guidance and support and to Claire Burnill for checking on a couple of the pieces. Thanks also to the members of the Wakefield Circuit for field testing some of the material.

Contents

October

November

December

Introduction

I can quite clearly remember my first encounter with drama in church. It was in the mid-1970s and in those days anything that had even the faintest whiff of the dramatic about it was frowned upon as being 'not quite serious enough for worship'. It was all thought to be slightly frivolous. The early books of sketches for use in church worship used to contain lengthy essays justifying the use of drama on biblical grounds. We used to perform drama in youth services at my home church of Leatherhead in Surrey (because that was the only place where you could get away with it). It was a revelation to me. I suddenly realized that humour could be employed in worship. My friends and I who had grown up on *Monty Python* and *The Two Ronnies* saw that being slightly silly could be an excellent way of pressing home a point or conveying a message. We started writing sketches for use in school assemblies (Therfield Comprehensive was never to be the same again) – and everything felt very daring and new.

Thank goodness that we have moved on from those days. In an era of visual communication and quick sound bites, drama is an excellent way of conveying ideas and truth. It captures the imagination, centres concentration, opens up new lines of thought and enables things to be said that might be quite difficult in any other format. It is a useful and versatile tool for developing ideas in a very concentrated, concise form, combining the verbal and visual in a unique way.

The special occasions covered by the sketches in this book are particularly suited to drama. There are often very strong themes that need to be conveyed at these events and drama is an excellent way of opening up those themes. They will sit easily with a range of biblical material chosen specifically to emphasize the issues of the day.

The dialogue dramas in this book try to be as 'user friendly' as possible. They include a minimum of props, and elaborate costumes, while fun, are not necessary. I have kept the sketches as dialogues so that even smaller churches and fellowship groups can have a go at doing them. When performing, try to remember that people need time to process thoughts and ideas, so speak more slowly than you think is necessary and prepare them carefully beforehand.

Finally, do enjoy performing these pieces – I had great fun writing them!

Paul S. Glass

How complicated

(Vera walks across the front, followed by Hilda)

Hilda: Oh hello Vera, love. How are you?

Vera: Mustn't complain, Hilda, mustn't complain. Actually, I've got quite a big weekend coming up.

Hilda: Oh, do tell. What's up? Your Trevor going bungee jumping again, is he?

Vera: No, love – he's only just got the cast off from last time. He's been so difficult to live with. Like a spoilt little boy. I mean, it was only a compound fracture in six places. If only the cord had been shorter he'd have been all right.

Hilda: So if it's not Trevor – 'cos it almost always is Trevor, isn't it?

Vera: It is, love, it is.

Hilda: Then what is it?

Vera: Well, you know our Tracy's getting married in the summer?

Hilda: Oh, it's the talk of the town.

Vera: Yeah well, the vicar's saying he wants 'em to go to church before the wedding – you know, show willing like.

Hilda: So, you're all going, are you?

Vera: Well, there's about fifteen of us, yeah.

Hilda: Oh, I love church – all them lovely hymns like what Aled Jones sings on the telly. So which church is it then? The one down the bottom of the street?

Vera: You know, I'm not sure. I never asked.

Hilda: Well, the one down the bottom of the street, that's a Methodist, isn't it?

Vera: Is it? What's that then? Methodist?

Hilda: Well, they're called that 'cos they've got, like, a different 'method' of doing things, haven't they?

Vera: Have they?

Hilda: Oh yeah, an' they have nothing but coffee mornings.

Vera: So they're a different religion then?

Hilda: No – they're all still Christians, aren't they?

Vera: Well, I'm not Christian, I'm Church of England.

Hilda: You plonker, they're Christian too.

Vera: Are you sure? I thought the Queen was one?

Hilda: She is – she's the head person.

Vera: So what's it got to do with God then? Never mind, what's that church up Green Street?

Hilda: That's the Baptist Church.

Vera: So what do they believe?

Hilda: Pretty much the same as everybody else but their vicar's got a guitar. He goes into our Sandra's school and does assemblies.

Vera: This is getting me all confused. What about the church by Tesco?

Hilda: That's the Roman Catholics.

Vera: Oh, they've got a really good game of bingo on a Saturday night. But I don't think they'll be getting married there. Steve's not a Catholic.

Hilda: Well, will it be at the United Reformed Church up on Yew Tree Drive?

Vera: Oh, I don't know. This is all so confusing. Methodist, Church of England, Baptist, Catholic, United Reformed …

Hilda: And don't forget the Salvation Army and the Evangelical Church on Sycamore Crescent.

Vera: Don't they all believe in the same thing?

Hilda: Pretty much, yeah.

Vera: An' don't they all want us to think about God an' Jesus?

Hilda: Absolutely.

Vera: So why are they making it so confusing? I thought Christianity was meant to be easy to understand.

Hilda: So did I Vera, so did I.

An offer you can't refuse

(A market trader stands centrally and tries to attract business)

Trader: Roll up, roll up, ladies and gentlemen. Look at what I've got for you this morning. Never offered before, and what a bargain it is. I can absolutely guarantee you've never seen anything like this ever. It will completely astound you. You will say to yourselves, 'How can I have lived without this up until now?' *(customer enters and approaches)* Ah, madam – how can you resist the bargain of the decade, nay, the century? Come closer.

Customer: So what is it then?

Trader: First of all, madam ... can I ask you just one very simple question?

Customer: I suppose so.

Trader: The simple question is this ... are you bored on Sunday mornings? I mean, yes, I know once a month in the summer you battle your way through the car boot sale, but be honest with me, madam – don't you find Sunday mornings just a little bit tedious? A tad dull?

Customer: Well, I ...

Trader: Of course you do. And I've got just the trick here. You'll have walked past your local churches and thought, 'I wonder what goes on in there?' But there's so many of them. The choice is so confusing – you end up going to none of them, am I right?

Customer: I, ah ...

Trader: Of course I am. Well, let me take all of that confusion away.

Customer: How?

Trader: Easy ... I have here, in easy-to-sample packages, your actual denominations. Why bother traipsing down to your local church to find out what goes on there when you can sample all you need to know right here?

Customer: Ooohh, that *does* sound interesting.

Trader: Of course it does. I've got your Anglican, I've got your Roman Catholic, I've got your Methodist, I've got your Charismatic free house church. And I'm giving them away at the measly price of £8.99 each or £14 for two.

Customer: So how does it work?

Trader: I'm glad you asked me that, madam, very glad indeed. I can tell you are a discriminating shopper. Well, let's say you think to yourself, 'Well, I think I might be Church of England, let's try that first', you just buy my trusty Church of England taster and you'll have all you need to know. There's four of the Thirty-nine Articles ... just to give you an idea. There's a tape of a typical PCC meeting, there's a little model of a choirboy complete with surplice, and there's an English Heritage order listing your local parish church.

Customer: That sounds lovely.

Trader: Oh it is, madam, it is. Or say you think, 'What about the Roman Catholics?' With my little sampler you've got all you need to know. There's the soft smell of incense, a little model of a Jesuit, three candles, and a make-it-yourself model of a confessional.

Customer: What about the others?

Trader: Well, in the Methodist pack you've got a ceramic model of John Wesley, the tape of fifteen different hymns by Wesley and Watts, and the model agendas of the nine different meetings you'll be expected to go to as soon as you walk through the door. For the Baptists, there's your own little baptistry and pair of waders; for the Salvation Army a little tambourine; and for the charismatic house church there's a little figure of a person with their arms up in the air and a free subscription to The God Channel.

Customer: It all seems a little bit confusing.

Trader: It *is* a little, madam ... I'll give you that. But let's make it clear that despite their faults and failings, despite their little quirks — and there's a lot of them — in every one of these churches you can truly and wonderfully worship God, the creator of the entire universe.

Customer: You can?

Trader: Oh yes, and despite how it seems sometimes, they know that about each other as well.

Customer: Well, I think I'll take one of each.

Trader: See ... I knew you were a lady of taste.

Superchristian

(Voiceover person stands centrally – dramatic music is played – perhaps the theme from 'Jaws' – the start is as melodramatic as possible)

Voiceover: It was a time of desperation. It was an age of chaos. The very fabric of society seemed to be fraying at the edges. Children cried, babies screamed, it appeared as if there was nothing anyone could do to stem the tide of despair. The gossamer-thin strands of decency and justice which hold our world together were wearing thin. Humanity was in need of a hero. And then one stormy night the most unexpected of champions appeared in the most unlikely of places. In a church just outside Epsom something remarkable took place *(Herbert enters – he is weedy and wears spectacles)* – the world was given a new breed of hero. *(Herbert tugs at the sleeve of Voiceover person)*

Herbert: Ah ... is this ... ah, is this my bit?

Voiceover: Yes, indeed. Mild-mannered, weak, nerdish and timid Herbert Grizzlewold became the hero our world needed.

Herbert: I did?

Voiceover: Yes, you did. Herbert Grizzlewold became *Superchristian* – dedicated to justice, and the Prince of Peace.

Herbert: Ta-da!

Voiceover: Yes, Herbert Grizzlewold, in his normal life dedicated to nothing more than getting through life without getting hit too many times, and desperately in love, from a distance, with his girlfriend Cynthia ...

Herbert: Well, she would be my girlfriend if I could gather up the courage to tell her how I feel.

Voiceover: Yes, yes. Of course. This very same nine-stone weakling was that mighty hero Superchristian, dedicated servant of peace, justice and his mother's apple pies. But soon our hero was faced with a task so difficult, so dangerous, potentially so life-threatening that only a hero of his calibre and bravery would even think about trying to tackle it.

Herbert: The churches. There are just so many of them and they're so divided.

Voiceover: You said it ...

Herbert: I've just asked the Methodists and the Baptists to come along to a meeting at the parish church to talk about mission in this area.

Voiceover: And?

Herbert: The Methodists have got a committee meeting and the Baptists have got a house group.

Voiceover: What about the Catholics?

Herbert: Well, they can come but they won't arrive until after their midweek service has finished.

Voiceover: Even your super-hero powers will be stretched to the limit on this one.

Herbert: You're not kidding.

Voiceover: And so Herbert Grizzlewold, a.k.a. Superchristian, took on his most fearsome challenge yet. Trying to get Christians to work together. It wasn't easy …

Herbert: I've persuaded the Anglicans to come along but the Methodists have called a Church Council meeting to talk about it.

Voiceover: As soon as one obstacle was seemingly overcome, another would rear its head.

Herbert: Now the Catholics can come but the Baptists can't. It's almost as if they don't want to work together.

Voiceover: The local Churches Together meeting had passed a statement saying, 'We will only do separately what we cannot do together.'

Herbert: If only they actually meant it. I'm afraid super-strength and being able to fly are no match for this knotty problem.

Voiceover: And, indeed, the problem was exceedingly knotty. So knotty in fact that for the first time in his life Superchristian had to admit that he didn't know what to do next.

Herbert: Until I read John 17 verse 21.

Voiceover: Oh yes?

Herbert: *(reading from Bible)* 'I pray that they can be one. As you are in me and I am in you, I pray that they can also be one in us.'

Voiceover: And that means?

Herbert: That I'm not going to become downhearted and I'm never going to stop trying, because unity is what God wants.

Voiceover: And with that, Superchristian soared into the morning sunlight to continue his battle for love, justice, peace and Christian unity.

The driving lesson

(Two people sit on chairs – they are in a car – one a learner driver, the other a rather severe instructor)

Mr Critchley: Now then, Mr Foster, remember what I just said – the most important thing is, mirror, signal, manoeuvre. So are we ready to move out? Okay, off we go. *(they move into traffic)* That's good, now I want you to turn left here. Start indicating, that's it. Have you spotted that car that's racing up behind us? I … *(the car obviously passes them and cuts left – the instructor winds down the window).* You stupid fool, can't you see this is a learner driver? Are you mad or just blind? What did you have for breakfast this morning? Idiot pills? *(turning to Mr Foster)* Sorry about that.

Mr Foster: Is that the way to interact with other motorists?

Mr Critchley: Absolutely – you can learn a lot from me. Give them an inch and they'll take a mile. You've got to hold your ground, Mr Foster, 'never give in', that's my motto. Yes – take notes from me and you'll learn a lot.

Mr Foster: But I thought most incidents of road rage were due to angry outbursts.

Mr Critchley: Ha! Experts … what do they know? This is the school of hard knocks out here you know, Foster. It's eat or be eaten. Now, let's continue. Yes, down here to the 'T' junction. Why on earth are you slowing down, Mr Foster?

Mr Foster: Well, there's an elderly lady on that zebra crossing ahead of us.

Mr Critchley: So? That doesn't mean you slow down, you timid little man. Watch and learn *(leans out of window)* – get out of the way you silly old fool! Come on, come on – we get five points for a little old lady, you know! I could have died waiting for you to cross this road … get on with it!

Mr Foster: What do you think you're doing?

Mr Critchley: Clearing the road for the motorist … you can look on it as a public service, you know.

Mr Foster: But that's terrible … you said we got five points.

Mr Critchley: Absolutely, five points for scaring elderly ladies, fifteen points for horrible little ten-year-olds, fifty points for traffic wardens, and seventy-five points for knocking down speed cameras.

Mr Foster: That's appalling.

Mr Critchley: Oh, get a grip, Mr Foster – this is the real world we're in, not some kind of namby-pamby fantasy. I'm going to educate you on the rules of the road: never give way, always blast your horn and never slow down on an amber light – always speed up.

Mr Foster: I thought you were a good instructor.

Mr Critchley: I am … best for miles around, because I tell you how things *really* are.

Mr Foster: Well I think that's awful.

Mr Critchley: Yeah, well, you would. No backbone. You sit there and you expect it all to be nice and easy. No graft, no difficulty. Well this is the school of hard knocks, this is an education you won't get anywhere else, these are the lessons you need to learn, matey, and I'm the person you need to listen to.

Mr Foster: No … you're not.

Mr Critchley: I beg your pardon?

Mr Foster: I don't have to listen to you. I don't have to learn from you. I've got other choices. You don't get it, do you? We choose what voices we listen to, who we learn from, who we decide to be influenced by. And I choose not to be influenced by you, not to be educated by you. We're through Mr Critchley … goodbye. *(gets out of car)*

Mr Critchley: You're going to regret this, you know. I'm the finest teacher around. I've got the lessons you need – I'm the only person worth listening to. Wait … come back! *(addresses audience)* That's the third pupil I've lost this week – can't understand it.

A responsive dialogue

(Two people stand centrally)

Actor 1: Greetings to you … my colleague and I are here this morning to facilitate a relevant and responsive dialogue regarding a strategic overview of our client-based services, with a view to focusing on outcomes, evaluating brokerage opportunities, in a flexible, user-led, target-setting delivery scenario.

Actor 2: *(translating)* We're here to have a chat.

Actor 1: During our presentation we will be modelling the delivery of high quality, interagency based, multi-disciplinary, strategic interventions for the benefit of our target audience.

Actor 2: We'll be serving tea and coffee later, and if you're lucky chocolate chip cookies.

Actor 1: At all times our delivery will be flexible, strategically planned and delivered to maximise potential, delivering high quality outcomes, enhancing and engaging with our user groups and modelling best practice at all opportunities.

Actor 2: We'll try and keep it interesting, but we're promising nothing.

Actor 1: This approach has been developed to enhance the sustainability and influence of our key players with a prime focus on evaluation, development and appropriate reflection.

Actor 2: We're talking to *you.*

Actor 1: We need to establish and maintain credibility with all stakeholders and implement review outputs.

Actor 2: I have no idea what that means.

Actor 1: Sustaining user involvement and strategic planning at all levels of our outcome-based approach.

Actor 2: Is this even English?

Actor 1: Of course, the paradigm of user interfaces and resource intensiveness of participation is paramount at all times.

Actor 2: Perhaps I've just landed on another planet.

Actor 1: And of course USPs – User Selling Points – are crucial to all of our strategies and inclusive ways of working ...

Actor 2: ... or perhaps I'm in a parallel dimension.

Actor 1: So without further ado let us task ourselves to become motivationally enhanced and tackle all negativity in a global scenario of non-acceptance.

Actor 2: Okay ... this has gone far enough. My head is swimming. What on earth are you going on about?

Actor 1: I'm sorry?

Actor 2: Do you honestly think that what you just said means anything?

Actor 1: I was just trying to use the latest terminology.

Actor 2: You were just trying to drive me mad is what you were doing.

Actor 1: Well I'm sorry, but if the Church in its educating is going to be at the forefront we need to use all the latest ...

Actor 2: Jargon? No, I don't think so. What does it say in the New Testament about the teaching of Jesus?

Actor 1: Ah ...

Actor 2: Come on, you know this.

Actor 1: That the people heard him gladly.

Actor 2: Absolutely, and?

Actor 1: They were amazed at his authority.

Actor 2: They understood him, they knew what he was talking about, because he wasn't like the scribes and the teachers of the law.

Actor 1: Ah ...

Actor 2: Exactly, 'ah'. Now, what do you think you just sounded like? Jesus or a teacher of the law?

Actor 1: Oh ...

Actor 2: Indeed ... oh. Perhaps it's time to start again. Because if we're to learn anything the first step is at least to understand.

Lamberton and Phipps on education

(Phipps is a 1930s butler, Lamberton his employer)

Lamberton:	I say, Phipps.
Phipps:	You called, my lord?
Lamberton:	I did indeed, I've just had the most splendid invitation in the post.
Phipps:	How pleasing for you, sir. *(pause)*
Lamberton:	Well, dash it all, Phipps, aren't you going to ask me what it's an invitation for?
Phipps:	Pardon me, sir. I had not realized you wanted the conversation to continue. What is it for?
Lamberton:	Well, Phipps old boy, I'll be blowed if it isn't an invite to attend a school reunion. Ah yes, the old crowd at St Oswald's Academy for the Permanently Posh. We even had a sign over the door saying, 'no riff-raff'.
Phipps:	How open-minded, sir.
Lamberton:	Indeed, and all my old chums – my companions in mischievous japes. There was 'Basher' Harris, 'Nosher' Etheridge, 'Chipper' Simms and me. What times we had – what jolliness ensued whenever we were together.
Phipps:	I'm sure it was one long round of excitement and fun, sir.
Lamberton:	It was indeed, Phipps my old friend, it was indeed. Why, I can still remember the prank which involved three tubs of lard, an unwitting first year, several balls of twine and the school laundry shoot.
Phipps:	I hope the person involved was not scarred for life.
Lamberton:	Oh, I very much doubt it, Phipps – although as I recall a psychologist did have to be called. Anyway – I must go along to this reunion and relive those wonderful days of school.
Phipps:	And to talk about the glories of the education you received, no doubt.
Lamberton:	I'm sorry, Phipps, what was that?
Phipps:	Well, the purpose of school, surely, sir, is to educate. To open minds to the glories and wonders of knowledge.
Lamberton:	Well, I dare say some of that went on, Phipps, but my friends and I were far too busy pulling off wizard wheezes to take much notice.

Phipps:	So the Herculean efforts of the staff to open your mind to the wonders of the world failed, sir?
Lamberton:	Well, I ah … the staff themselves were an excellent lot, Phipps, hard-working, long-suffering, dedicated, enthusiastic.
Phipps:	I do not doubt it, sir. It just seems odd, does it not?
Lamberton:	What seems odd, Phipps?
Phipps:	Well, sir. If I may be so bold. We have minds given to us by God and the potential, through excellent schools and universities, to make the best of those minds, to educate ourselves in matters physical and spiritual.
Lamberton:	I say, Phipps, steady on.
Phipps:	And yet, sir, we waste those opportunities, we squander them and we take every chance we have to belittle those who seek to broaden their minds.
Lamberton:	Well, I never did.
Phipps:	It just seems to me, sir, that there are millions of people all over the world who would love to have the opportunity for education that we have had. And no doubt they would make better use of that gift than we have done.
Lamberton:	Well, I say, Phipps. What an extraordinary outburst.
Phipps:	I know, sir, and I am sorry.
Lamberton:	No, by George, don't be. Education is precious, very precious. Making the most of God-given minds and all that … crucial. You've opened my eyes today, Phipps, and I thank you for it.
Phipps:	It was my pleasure, sir.
Lamberton:	Should be thankful for the teachers I had – geography, science, declining Latin verbs, the perfect puff pastry – all vital educational stuff, Phipps.
Phipps:	Indeed, sir.
Lamberton:	Not appreciative enough in my school days, Phipps. Not thankful enough.
Phipps:	No, sir.
Lamberton:	Tell you what – I'll insist that all the staff are invited to the reunion – we'll throw them a big old 'thank you' party.
Phipps:	That would be wonderful, sir.
Lamberton:	Education is a pretty stunning thing, eh, Phipps?
Phipps:	It certainly is, sir. It certainly is.

Ralph and Jim on refugees

(Ralph and Jim sit – as if at a table in a pub)

Ralph: So then, Jim mate, I was reading in the *Daily Scum* the other day ...

Jim: You know what, Ralph mate, before you start to tell me about your in-depth reading, I just wanted to say that I've always found the *Daily Scum* to be a paragon of reporting excellence. Their commitment to in-depth journalism is stunning, you can always believe every single word you read ...

Ralph: And there's always pictures of scantily clad ladies ...

Jim: Yeah well, that too. But their dedication to covering the bed-hopping antics of minor celebrities everywhere is outstanding.

Ralph: Well, as I was going to say ...

Jim: Sorry for interrupting you, Ralph mate.

Ralph: That's not a problem, Jim. Now, as I was saying, I've been reading what the *Scum* has to say on the controversial subject of refugees and asylum seekers.

Jim: I've always found the *Scum* to be level-headed and reasonable on that issue, Ralph.

Ralph: Oh yeah, no attempt at all to incite hatred, unreasonable fear or blind unthinking prejudice in the pages of the *Scum*, mate, as evidenced by this fair and unbiased headline: 'Send the Spongers Home.'

Jim: Oh ...

Ralph: What do you mean 'oh'?

Jim: Well, after so recently having praised the high levels of journalism in the aforementioned *Scum* I have to take exception to that headline.

Ralph: And why is that then, Jim mate?

Jim: Well, as everybody knows, Ralph, only 0.5 per cent of those claiming government benefits are asylum seekers.

Ralph: Oh ... that sounds like quite a small number, Jim.

Jim: It is, Ralphy boy, it is. Most asylum seekers come to this country from war-torn countries like Somalia, they're not economic migrants at all.

Ralph: 'Oh' again.

Jim: Indeed. When you think of the horrendous journey that most asylum seekers have had to get here, and when you think of the persecution they must have been suffering to go through with such a journey, well, it just makes you think.

Ralph: It's beginning to get me questioning the truth of the tabloid press, Jim mate.

Jim: Well, there's a stunner, Ralph. Oh, and there's one more thing that's got me brain going. And that is the question of Holy Writ.

Ralph: Holy What?

Jim: The Bible, Ralph mate.

Ralph: Oh.

Jim: It says quite clearly, Ralph, in the book of Exodus, chapter 23, 'Do not oppress the alien, for you know how it feels to be an alien; you yourselves were aliens in Egypt.'

Ralph: And that means what, exactly?

Jim: Well, as I understand it, Ralph mate, that's God saying to us, absolutely everybody on this planet is my much loved, highly praised creation. So treat 'em that way. You plonkers.

Ralph: Do you think God said the 'you plonkers' bit?

Jim: Oh no, mate, that was my own poetic licence.

Ralph: And it was very good. Well, Jim mate, you've given me pause for thought there. It would appear that the British press are not quite the paragons of honesty that I took them for.

Jim: Apparently not, Ralph. It appears we'll need to find out the truth about asylum seekers and refugees for ourselves.

Ralph: I'm up for it if you are, Jim.

Jim: Lead the way, Ralphy boy, lead the way.

A community in the night

(DJ sits on one side – broadcasting. Kate sits at the other – at home)

DJ: To all of you lonely souls out there just trying to get through the night, greetings. You're listening to Steve Carter with some fine music chosen especially for you. And if I can do anything to connect a couple of you searchers out there, drop me a line. You know where I am.

Kate: *(to the audience)* Well, I suppose I need to start my story somewhere. I loved listening to the Steve Carter show. He was on from 10 p.m. till 1 in the morning five nights a week. He broadcast from a ship somewhere out in the North Sea. And, somehow, knowing that he was out there on the high seas made the whole thing more intimate.

DJ: I've had an e-mail from Sophie who works on the checkouts at Tesco in Wisbech, Cambridgeshire. She's twenty-seven with dark hair, and a great sense of humour. She loves movies, cats and line-dancing and would be very interested in meeting someone with similar tastes.

Kate: Steve was interested in making connections between people, in building relationships. As we sat in our rooms making our community of lonely people in the night, somehow we felt as though we were connected with each other. I know it sounds a little strange, but Steve voiced our hopes and fears and brought us together.

DJ: Harold is sixty-five years old and lives in Southampton. He's been a widower for two years now and is pretty lonely. He's into walks in the country, going dancing and stockcar racing. Anybody out there in the night interested? Let me know.

Kate: Because that's what's important, isn't it? Finding love, being loved. Despite all the corny, hackneyed, clichéd things that are said about it – it is love that we search for – love that we need.

DJ: Jane is thirty-four and a teacher. She lives in Doncaster. She freely admits that she's been so busy pursuing her career for the past few years that relationships haven't been possible. She's suddenly stopped and has looked around at her life and is beginning to wonder what she's been doing with her time. Jane enjoys going to the theatre, windsurfing and cooking. Jane, I hope you find what you're looking for very soon.

Kate: I know that God is love, of course I do. I know that Jesus shows us what that love is like, and that it is more precious than anything else in my life. I *know* that. But that doesn't mean that I'm not lonely sometimes, that I don't feel the need to experience love here and now. I believe that love is the most important thing in the world and that all of us need to experience it and share it and enjoy it.

DJ: And just before I sign off, there's time for one more. *(as she listens to this Kate buries her head in her hands)* Kate is fifty-five and lives in Liverpool. She's a Christian and works in the NHS. Kate enjoys walking her dog, reading novels and singing in a local choir. She also likes eating out – especially when there's somebody special to eat out with. It would be great if there was somebody out there for Kate tonight. Drop me a line, you know where to find me.

Kate: Well ... here's hoping, eh?

The theory

(Presenter and Professor sit as in an interview)

Presenter: Good evening, ladies and gentlemen, and welcome to yet another arty discussion programme on some satellite channel that only three people are watching. Tonight we're delighted to have with us Professor Stanley Albright who claims that he has a fascinating new theory about love. Good evening, professor.

Professor: *(rather absent-minded)* Good evening.

Presenter: So then, Professor, tell us all.

Professor: About what?

Presenter: I thought you had a new theory.

Professor: Do I?

Presenter: Well, I was told so.

Professor: Oh good, what is it?

Presenter: Ah ... it's about love, isn't it?

Professor: Is it? ... Oh yes! I remember now. Yes, I do have a theory.

Presenter: Good.

Professor: It's very exciting. It's taken years of research.

Presenter: I see.

Professor: And cost hundreds of thousands of pounds to compile.

Presenter: Wonderful.

Professor: And it's all mine.

Presenter: Lovely.

Professor: It will revolutionize the way we look at love and human relationships.

Presenter: Could you tell us what it is?

Professor: Oh yes, I'd better tell you what it is, hadn't I?

Presenter: Yes.

Professor: Well, my theory is ...

Presenter: Yes?

Professor: *(pause for effect)* That being in love is very nice.

Presenter: *(pause)* And?

Professor: Well, that's it really.

Presenter: So let me get this straight, Professor. Your theory is that love is very nice.

Professor: Very nice indeed, yes.

Presenter: And this has taken years of research and hundreds of thousands of pounds of tax-payers' money to come up with.

Professor: You don't sound very impressed.

Presenter: Well, that's because I'm not.

Professor: Oh dear.

Presenter: I mean, I could have told you that for nothing. What would have been interesting would have been if you'd come up with a new theory about God and love.

Professor: Well, I'm not sure ...

Presenter: I mean, here we have a world which is obsessed with romantic love, the charts are full of songs about it, magazines are crammed full with articles about it, but surely God offers us a far tougher and deeper view of what love might be about?

Professor: God does?

Presenter: Well, of course. We have Jesus coming into the world showing an open, radical, far-reaching way of love and then he dies – some say as an act of sacrificial love. Now that's a theory of love worth talking about, isn't it, Professor?

Professor: So you're not interested in my theory?

Presenter: Not at all.

Professor: Even though love is very, very nice.

Presenter: Professor, that's the least interesting thing about it.

Professor: Oh my ... well, it's back to the drawing board, I suppose.

Presenter: And don't come back till you've got something interesting to tell us.

Pray

(Mary stands centrally, enter Martha)

Martha: Oh Mary, there you are. Where have you been? No, never mind. You should have been here half an hour ago. There's so much to do you wouldn't believe it.

Mary: Oh, I think I would.

Martha: There's been food to buy and prepare, cleaning to do, invitations to send out. And, as usual, you've been no help, no help at all.

Mary: Martha, calm down, everything will be all right.

Martha: Only because I've slaved over the preparations night and day for two weeks. If the ministry of Jesus is going to move forward – if we're to have any impact at all on the important and influential people we've got coming tonight then we must make a good first impression. It's vital that Jesus is heard and understood by as many people as possible.

Mary: And he will be Martha, he will be.

Martha: By the way, where is he?

Mary: Where's who?

Martha: Now don't be deliberately dense, Mary. Jesus, of course.

Mary: Oh, he went off for a walk up into the hills.

Martha: He did what? Did he say where he was going? What he was doing? When he expected to be back? Had he already prepared a speech for tonight?

Mary: Look, I have no idea. All I know is that he left about an hour ago.

Martha: Well, did he say why he'd walked out on us?

Mary: He said he was going to find a quiet place to pray.

Martha: To pray? Why on earth does he want to pray at a time like this? There are things to do, people to meet, lives to change. He can't do any of that if he's praying.

Mary: Martha, have you ever considered that he couldn't do any of that if he *doesn't* pray?

Martha: What? Look, there's action to be taken, things to do.

Mary: And that action is only God centred if it's prayed through first.

Martha: This is ridiculous.

Mary: No, it's not, Martha. Look, I love you completely. You're my sister. But you drive me mad sometimes. Everything's got to be action with you, events, lists, things to do.

Martha: Well, nothing around here would get done without it.

Mary: I know that, but have you ever wondered whether it was God's action you were involved in or your own?

Martha: Well, God's, of course.

Mary: How do you know? You never ask him.

Martha: What?

Mary: When was the last time you sat and prayed? Properly prayed? Too much like hard work I guess. You'd far rather be off changing the world. But if you don't sit with God, share time, build a relationship – how can you know you're changing in the right way?

Martha: I ... I just find prayer so difficult, that's all.

Mary: Well, why didn't you say so? We can do it together. I'll help you.

Martha: I would like to change things.

Mary: That's wonderful, and I'll help with the preparations round the house. Don't worry, everything's going to be all right.

The plan

(There is a laptop computer on a table – two people enter furtively and approach it)

Spy 1:   *(looking around)* So, is *he* around?

Spy 2:   Well, technically – since the being referred to is almighty God – sex doesn't come into it. We're talking about God here – 'he' could be a 'she' ...

Spy 1:   All right, all right. Let's just accept that it's convenient shorthand. Is he around?

Spy 2:   Well, again, technically, since God is omnipresent, he's always around.

Spy 1:   *(getting exasperated)* We haven't got time for this. Can you see God?

Spy 2:   Ah well, that's a metaphysical question ...

Spy 1:   Will you be quiet!

Spy 2:   Sorry ... and in answer to your question, no, he's not here at the moment, he's doing a spot of in-service training for archangels.

Spy 1:   Good, then we can steal some of his design secrets. Let's see what he's been working on *(sits down at laptop and looks at screen)* Ah ha!

Spy 2:   What is it?

Spy 1:   I have no idea.

Spy 2:   It looks like he's been working on something called 'a mother'.

Spy 1:   Yes, but look. This has got to be wrong. According to this mothers have eyes in the backs of their heads.

Spy 2:   And the ability to get a two-year-old child to wash behind their ears ... impossible.

Spy 1:   Let's scroll down a bit more. *(operates laptop)*

Spy 2:   *(reading)* Never-ending supply of love and hugs ...

Spy 1:   Ability to see through children's bedroom doors so when she asks, 'What are you doing in there?' she already knows.

Spy 2:   Six pairs of hands for binding scraped knees and cooking tea all at the same time.

Spy 1:   This is ludicrous, he cannot be serious.

Spy 2:   Ability to wipe crayon off bathroom tiles and keep smiling.

Spy 1:   And look at this, tough enough to take the heartbreak that sometimes comes with raising children whilst also being soft enough to have a shoulder to cry on at all times of the day or night.

Spy 2:   This is amazing. Look, the ability to care for sick children whilst feeling pretty rough herself.

Spy 1:   And completely unselfish – putting the needs of her family above her own time and time again.

Spy 2:   An ability to care for teenagers without going mad …

Spy 1:   *(looking up)* Oh, he's bitten off more than he can chew this time. Even God can't achieve this.

Spy 2:   *(reading screen)* Look, it leaks too.

Spy 1:   That's not a leak, you fool, it's a tear. Tears of love and joy. Tears as the first child goes to school, at the broken heart of her teenager, at the graduation ceremony and the wedding.

Spy 2:   This is amazing.

Spy 1:   It's wonderful. Think how our lives would have been different if we'd had somebody like that.

Spy 2:   *(beginning to cry)* Mummy!

Spy 1:   Look, we're never going to able to duplicate this.

Spy 2:   We could try.

Spy 1:   What … and risk getting the whole thing terribly wrong? He doesn't even supply them with an instruction booklet.

Spy 2:   No, I suppose that's why he's all-powerful and we're idiots.

Spy 1:   Exactly. Let's see if there's anything else in here we can nick … *(looks at computer)*

Spy 2:   *(looking at screen)* Ah, TV celebrity chef … that should be a little easier.

Action Time – on mothers

(Two children's TV presenters sit centrally – hugely enthusiastic)

Chris: Hello everybody and welcome to *Action Time*! I'm Chris.

Jane: And I'm Jane.

Chris and
Jane: Hello!

Chris: Well, we all know what's special this weekend, don't we?

Jane: Yes, it's Mothering Sunday!

Chris: And in honour of that special day Jane is going to go into the kitchen later on in the programme to make our *Action Time* special sticky chocolate, toffee, marshmallow and sugar Sunday treats. Don't worry about the fact that your mum's on a diet ... she'll just love them.

Jane: That's right ... it'll be great! And Chris will be showing you how to make a really special Mothering Sunday gift using only three rolls of sticky back plastic, a tube of glitter, a pair of surgical scissors and a feather duster.

Chris: You'll be amazed!

Jane: And your mum will love it!

Chris: *(turning to Jane, as if the TV cameras have been turned off)* So what are you going to do for your mum on Sunday, Jane?

Jane: What do you mean, Chris?

Chris: Well, are you going to take her out for a slap-up lunch, or make her breakfast, or get her a lovely card, or send her an extravagant bunch of flowers?

Jane: Uh ... none of the above, Chris.

Chris: Oh.

Jane: Look, Chris, I'm an important TV celebrity, I don't have time to go round pandering to my dear old mum. That's kids' stuff.

Chris: Uuhh, we work on a kids' TV show, Jane.

Jane: Exactly, Chris, that's why I'm too busy to do anything this year. I'm always bungee jumping over raging rivers, or abseiling down the sides of buildings or sky diving at thirty thousand feet.

Chris: But don't you feel we ought to be full of thanks for the wonderful love our mothers have shown us, Jane, and for all the sacrifices they've made on our behalf?

Jane: Well, duh, Chris. Of course I am, and the way that I can thank her is by being so driven and ambitious that I earn as much money as possible and become as famous as Elton John.

Chris: Don't you think she'd prefer to *see* you once in a while?

Jane: Look, Chris. I'd love to but I just don't have the time. My mum understands.

Chris: *(addressing audience)* Well, children, wasn't it interesting to find out what Jane thinks about her mother?

Jane: What?

Chris: Yes, Jane, we've been on camera the whole time and all the children watching just heard your little outburst about mothers.

Jane: Wait … no … I …

Chris: Too late to take it all back now, Jane. They've heard just how selfish, driven, ungrateful and shallow you truly are.

Jane: No … I didn't mean any of it. It was a joke. Come on, kids, you know when good old Jane's joking, don't you? Ha, ha. Mothers are really very special people.

Chris: Yes, they are. They love us, they care for us, they make tremendous sacrifices for us. It's good to say 'thank you' for love like that. You know, Jane, in their prayers, Christians are more and more referring to God as 'mother'. Because they realize in the love of a mother we're seeing a small picture of the way God loves us too.

Jane: *(hanging head)* Leave me alone.

Chris: Let's leave Jane now, children, as she watches her career slowly drift away. You're never too old to do something wonderful for your mum. To show how thankful you are, and that you recognize something of the love that she has shown to you. So be grateful – she deserves it. And that's it from this week's *Action Time*! So it's goodbye from me, Chris. And I think Jane says 'goodbye' too.

Jane: It was a joke, kids. A joke!

Mother Church

(Two actors stand centrally)

Voice 1:   The Church is like a mother to us.

Voice 2:   A what?

Voice 1:   A mother.

Voice 2:   No, it's not, the church is that redbrick building on the housing estate.

Voice 1:   It's also that rather grand but costly Victorian pile with a steeple down the road.

Voice 2:   It's even that large building in the centre of town that used to be a cinema but is being used by the Pentecostals now.

Voice 1:   It's also a humble mudbrick building in the middle of a remote village in Tanzania.

Voice 2:   Yes, it's all those things – so it can't be a mother.

Voice 1:   Why not?

Voice 2:   Because it's got four walls and a door, that's why not. It's a building.

Voice 1:   I'm not disputing the fact that it's a building.

Voice 2:   Thank goodness for that – at least there's something we agree on.

Voice 1:   Yes, there is. But it's more than just a building … it's a mother to us.

Voice 2:   You're just trying to wind me up now, aren't you? Admit it, this is some elaborate plot to get me to lose my cool. That's it, isn't it? You're messing with my head.

Voice 1:   Now, would I do that to you?

Voice 2:   Yes.

Voice 1:   I'm shocked that you'd even think that. Let's see if I can explain. Listen – what do you feel when you go to church?

Voice 2:   Cold.

Voice 1:   Now it's your turn to wind *me* up. Seriously, what do you feel?

Voice 2:   I feel accepted, loved, supported, cared for.

Voice 1: Uh huh.

Voice 2: What do you mean 'uh huh'?

Voice 1: Well, isn't that exactly how a *mother* makes you feel?

Voice 2: *(realizing)* Oh ... all right. So that's why the church is like a mother to us. So, don't tell me, now you're going to get all superior and 'I told you so' about it, aren't you?

Voice 1: Not at all. Christians over hundreds of years have talked about 'mother Church' – about a building that's more than a building. An institution that's more than an institution. At its best it has loved us when we have been unlovable ...

Voice 2: Cared for us when we have strayed ...

Voice 1: Always been there for us even though we sometimes haven't cared.

Voice 2: Wherever you go in the world, it's there.

Voice 1: With doors open wide in acceptance and love.

Voice 2: It's a deep relationship of trust and love.

Voice 1: And as long as Christ is at the centre of the Church then it's a relationship that will never let us go and will grow and develop over the years.

Voice 2: It's rather a nice picture, isn't it?

Voice 1: Yes, it is. And on a day like today it's a very helpful picture as well.

Voice 2: Why's that, then?

Voice 1: Well, it's Mothering Sunday.

Voice 2: What? Why didn't you tell me? A card, chocolates, flowers, I've done nothing! *(Runs off)*

Voice 1: Oh. Sorry about that. Anyway, to sum up, the Church is like a mother to us, and that ... unlike my friend ... can be depended upon.

On the doorstep

(Two actors move to the front – they are slightly over the top)

R.H.:   Good morning to you all.

W.F: Yes, a good morrow indeed.

R.H.:   My name is Royston Hansley.

W.F.:   And I am Willimina Farquhar.

R.H.:   And we are ... actors.

W.F.:   Indeed we are, and we – in the business that we call 'show' – would like to doff our collective cap to all of you.

R.H.:   Because it has come to our attention that you are about to embark on that most dangerous of occupations ...

W.F.:   That most enduring of ordeals ...

R.H.:   The house-to-house envelope collection.

W.F.:   And so, in honour of that event we would like to bring to you a small entertainment entitled, 'Adventures in Christian Aid Envelope Collecting'. In which I shall take on the part of the courageous Christian Aid envelope collector.

R.H.:   And I shall essay a number of character roles.

           (During the next part Royston puts on a variety of hats and glasses as he takes on each new role, Willimina moves as if from door to door, knocking on each one as she comes to it)

W.F.:   Knock, knock.

R.H.:   *(comes to the door in flat cap and jacket – rather abrupt)* Yes, what d'you want?

W.F.:   I've come to collect your Christian Aid envelope.

R.H.:   My what?

W.F.:   It looks like this.

R.H.:   Oh yes. No.

W.F.:   No?

R.H.:   No, I never give to people in Africa. They ought to sort out their own problems. Always starving. Went on a safari to Kenya once. Stayed in dashed good hotels. But no, I only give to Lifeboats and Guide Dogs. Charity begins at home, that's what I say. Spongers, the lot of them. Goodbye. *(slams door)*

W.F.:   I ... oh. *(to audience)* It's not always very easy is it? *(moves to next door)* Knock, knock.

R.H.:   *(comes to the door in pair of glasses)* Yes?

W.F.:   I've come to collect your Christian Aid envelope.

R.H.:   Oh ... ah ... have you put one through? Let's have a look. *(proceeds to search)* No, I'm pretty sure I haven't had one, sorry. It would be here on the mantelpiece.

W.F.:   Don't worry. I've got another one here.

R.H.:   *(obviously slightly disappointed)* Oh. Oh right. *(takes envelope, turns his back to her, fumbles in pocket for coppers – puts one in)*. There you go.

W.F.:   Thank you. *(closes door)* Then there are the sort who want a discussion on the doorstep. Knock, knock.

R.H.:   *(comes to the door with a very loud jacket on)* Ah yes. I know you. The Christian Aid collector. Now, how much of this is going to aid projects? Because I don't want any of it going on education, you know, or office expenses. All these charities, they're all alike. I mean they employ people, don't they? How dare they do that? And don't get me started on the campaigning side of things. Making the world a better place ... the cheek of it. I don't want to be told why the world is in such a mess, and I don't want to be told I've got to live more simply. No, no. I like my decadent western lifestyle, thank you very much.

W.F.:   I take it that's a 'no' then?

R.H.:   Don't interrupt me when I'm pontificating about something I haven't bothered to find out about.

W.F.:   Goodbye. *(closes door – comes back into character – addresses audience)* To all of you who collect for Christian Aid door to door, Royston and I salute you.

R.H.:   To those of you who have gone despite yapping dogs ...

W.F.:   And snappy people ...

R.H.:   Who have braved wind and rain ...

W.F.:   Who have stood on street corners with collecting tins.

R.H.:   We salute you.

W.F.:   You do much more than collect money.

R.H.:   You remind people that there is a big world out there.

W.F.:   A world of wonderful variety, brilliant diversity but also tremendous need.

R.H.:   A world that we cannot turn our backs on.

W.F.:   A world that we are part of.

R.H.:   And stewards of.

W.F.:   A world that needs us to play our part, day in and day out.

R.H.:   So that everybody can enjoy life.

W.F.:   The life that God has given us.

R.H.:   Each day and every day.

W.F.:   Amen.

R.H.:   Amen.

Carstairs and Frobisher

(Carstairs, an elderly explorer, sits centrally, writing)

Carstairs: 'And as I sat in my kayak racing down the Zambezee, careening towards the precipice of a deadly waterfall, I cast my eye around my small craft to see whether there was anything that could aid me in my plight and realized that I only possessed one small piece of string, three paper clips and an old copy of the *Radio Times* ...'

(enter Frobisher who walks across to Carstairs, hand outstretched)

Frobisher: Hello, name's Beatrice Frobisher, new member of the club. Sorry about the first name ... parents wanted a girl, kept me in skirts till I was six years old. Who do I have the pleasure of greeting?

Carstairs: Sir Archibald Carstairs, longest standing member of the 'Secret Daredevil Explorers and Silly Adventurers Club', pleasure to meet you.

Frobisher: If it doesn't seem too bold, may I ask what you're writing there?

Carstairs: Yes, of course, just completing the fourteenth volume of the extraordinary adventures of my life. Going to call this chapter, 'Saved by three paper clips and a copy of the *Radio Times* on the Zambezee'.

Frobisher: Ah, the Zambezee, know it well, spent twenty-five years travelling around Africa, wrestlin' rhinos, battlin' baboons, grapplin' with gorillas, dontcha' know? Happy days.

Carstairs: Yes, happy days.

Frobisher: You know, what I can't understand is when I read the newspapers these days and see all the trouble that there is over there. People going hungry, wars taking place, corruption – can't understand it.

Carstairs: No, my friend 'Basher' Harris drew them nice new national boundaries – even put a ruler on the map and drew straight down the line so we all knew where we were. 'Course, it did split tribes up and put mortal enemies against each other in the same country, but where would the Empire be without a bit of friendly rivalry, eh? A bit of competition? Never did me any harm at school.

Frobisher: Not one bit. And the hunger thing ... can't understand it. Just 'cos we took all the best land and then made them grow cash crops they have no earthly use for and paid them a pittance to do it – anybody would think it was our fault.

Carstairs: And as for the debt – what's wrong with a western bank lending them loads of money – and then taking more than the original loan in interest – knowing that they'll never be able to pay it back?

Frobisher: Dashed good business, I'd say.

Carstairs: Well, I've never understood finance myself. Left that to my cousin Archibald Fotherington Smythe the third, dashed good banker. Took half a dozen African countries for all they were worth.

Frobisher: Yes ... I can't be doing with money – rather get involved with a tidy little adventure involving a burning rope bridge, three hair brushes and some duct tape.

Carstairs: That sounds dashed exciting. Reminds me of the time when I was lashed to a raft in the middle of a river with a great big hippopotamus bearing down on me – about to have me for lunch. I looked around to see what I had to hand and there was only a stapler, three rubber bands and an old gramophone player.

Frobisher: Now that's what the real problems of Africa are all about.

Carstairs: Absolutely. Give me a slightly silly adventure any day of the week.

Frobisher: Well, it certainly beats dealing with reality.

Carstairs: Reality? Haven't been interested in it for years. Come along, old boy.

(they exit)

The debt interview

(A bank clerk sits at a table – enter a customer)

Clerk: Good morning, sir, welcome to the National Bank of Malawi.

Customer: Hold up your hands, this is a stick-up.

Clerk: I'm sorry?

Customer: I said, 'Hold up your hands, this is a stick-up.'

Clerk: Oh dear.

Customer: 'Oh dear' is right, mate – put all the money you've got in this sack here.

Clerk: What, the one with 'Debt Repayment' written in big letters on the side?

Customer: That's the one, yes.

Clerk: If you don't mind me saying so, sir, you don't look very much like a bank robber. You look far too smart.

Customer: That's because I'm a new breed of thief. I'm a high-ranking member of … *(with emphasis)* the World Big Bucks Corporation.

Clerk: *(shocked)* Not … the World Big Bucks Corporation?

Customer: The very same. And as we gave poor countries like you ill-advised loans ages ago and have been fleecing you for interest ever since, it shouldn't surprise you to know that now we've decided on a cunning new plan.

Clerk: Oh yes, and what's that?

Customer: It's called, 'Just give us all the money you've got, it'll make things easier in the long run.'

Clerk: It's rather a long name for a cunning plan.

Customer: Yes, but it is *very* cunning. So put all your money in this big sack and I'll be on my way.

Clerk: But this is the National Bank of Malawi – we're one of the poorest countries in the world.

Customer: I know, and I'm one of the richest institutions in the world with billions of dollars at my fingertips. It's a match made in heaven.

Clerk: But doesn't this all sound a little bit unfair?

Customer: Of course it's unfair ... this is banking. You didn't think I was going to let you off the money you owe me, did you?

Clerk: Well, I was kind of hoping.

Customer: And what would be the point in that?

Clerk: Well, I thought morally you might feel it was the right thing to do.

Customer: 'Morals', 'the right thing to do'? I don't understand.

Clerk: No, I don't suppose you do.

Customer: Anyway, we're wasting valuable time, and I can't stand around here all day chatting with you, I've got more dirt-poor countries to exploit. So all you need to do is put all the money you've got in here.

Clerk: Oh, all right, if you say so.

Customer: By the way, remind me what currency you use here.

Clerk: The Kwacha.

Customer: The Kwacha? Oh yes, I remember. How many of those do I get to the pound these days?

Clerk: About two hundred.

Customer: *(looking at notebook)* Two hundred? But three years ago it was one hundred.

Clerk: Yes, I'm afraid our currency is dropping in value all the time. It's because you've crippled our economy with debt repayments.

Customer: But that makes your currency almost valueless. You're hardly worth robbing at all.

Clerk: Hmmm, sad isn't it?

Customer: Oh, this is useless – you're no fun. I'm going to take my business elsewhere and rob somebody else.

Clerk: Well, if you must.

Customer: Huh ... you're just miserable. I'm off. *(leaves)*

Clerk: Bye. Wait a minute ... you forgot your sack ... ah, well ... back to the drawing board.

Pre-worship announcements

(Two actors – they are as close to air stewards doing a pre-flight set of announcements as possible)

Actor 1:   Good morning, and welcome to St Andrews Church this morning. We realize that you have a choice of worship facilitators and we thank you for selecting St Andrews for all your praising needs this morning. Please do take notice of the following instructions about our worship today. We realize that many of you will have worshipped before but the details of this church may differ from those you have been to previously, so please do pay close attention. In the little wooden tray in front of you you will find a small and rather battered hymn book, a prayer book and a Bible. Lifting your head up for a moment you will see a small board with numbers on it at the front of the church. Of course, at no point will anybody connected with our service this morning let you know what these numbers refer to and when to use them.

Actor 2:   You will also have been given a rather difficult to read piece of paper with some very small print on it. This is our notice sheet, detailing the things that may or may not be happening over the next few days in the life of this church. Of course, though we do ask for notices to be in by Wednesday there's always somebody who's late so there will be half a dozen notices that will be read out. Once the worship is fully under way we would ask that you remain comfortably seated at all times. Some of you may have been worried by recent reports of DVT or Decreasing Value Trends and want to move around the church. Please resist the urge to do so. At one or two points in the service you may notice that people around you are standing up. Of course, they will all be looking at you because you're still sitting down.

Actor 1:   Exit points are conveniently signposted here *(indicates)* and here. In the case of an emergency strip lighting in the floor will illuminate and lead you to the nearest exit. Of course, you may just prefer to pray. And please do remember your nearest exit may well be behind you – particularly for those of you who seem to like sitting on the back row.

Actor 2:   In the rare event of the worship losing spirituality at any point, you will all be asked to clap and whoop very loudly and shout 'Alleluia, amen!'. Should the service lose direction at any point please do feel free to let your mind wander for a few moments. By the time you return to us we'll be back on track.

Actor 1: In a little while our smiling stewards will pass amongst you with plates or bags. Feel free to give as much money as you can.

Actor 2: After the service refreshments will be served in little blue cups. I'm afraid that only tea and coffee are available – oh, and some rather watered down orange squash. We're sorry, but we've been running low and forgot to buy some more, but we just know you'll love our special church biscuits – that is, as long as the children haven't got to them first.

Actor 1: Our worship today is brought to you by our dedicated band of complete professionals. At least, that's what it says here. Our choir, organist, music group and preacher would be glad of your comments.

Actor 2: Well, actually, to be completely honest with you, they only want to hear from you if you've got something nice to say.

Actor 1: *(more serious)* And as we worship in this building this morning please do remember that we are doing what billions of Christians have done every day for the past two thousand years.

Actor 2: For this is none other than the very gate of heaven, and this morning, as at any time and in any place, be prepared to meet with God.

Hayley and Kirsty on dedication

(Two actors stand at the front)

Kirsty: So I was telling Chantrelle that she was a wimp.

Hayley: Were you, Kirsty?

Kirsty: Absolutely, Hayley. I mean, she's only had her ears pierced. I said to her, look, don't even think about telling me that that's, like, a brave thing to do, right? 'Cos it ain't. Unless you've had navel, ear, bottom lip, tongue and eyelid pierced then you're not even in my league, right? You ain't showing no dedication, I told her.

Hayley: But *I* haven't had all them piercings done.

Kirsty: No, but yeah, that's all right for you, innit? 'Cos you're, like, dedicated in other ways, ain't you?

Hayley: Am I?

Kirsty: Well, yeah. Look at the fact that you spent three hours having your nails done the other day. That's real dedication to nail art, that is.

Hayley: Yeah, I suppose it is. And I'm really dedicated to *EastEnders*.

Kirsty: There – you see. You're the only person I know who watches it, tapes it, watches it again, then watches the Sunday afternoon omnibus edition as well.

Hayley: And I get the *Sad Person Inside Soap* magazine so I know what's going to happen over the next two weeks as well. I live for *EastEnders,* I do.

Kirsty: I know you do, an' that, like, shows real dedication, dunnit?

Hayley: Yeah – I didn't know I was such a dedicated person. An' well, like, you're dedicated to fashion, ain't you, Kirsty?

Kirsty: Absolutely. I have to know what's what. 'Cos, like, the colours that are in this week were *so* out last week. I've had to change my whole wardrobe. And don't get me started on the accessories, right? 'Cos they're, like, a nightmare. Earrings, beads an' bangles, necklaces, rings, bags. It's all gotta be just right.

Hayley: And shoes.

Kirsty:	Ah, now that's my speciality subject, that is. Fifty-five pairs at last count, heels and low slung, boots in all colours. Don't even walk me within half a mile of a shoe shop 'cos I've just gotta go in there and once I'm there … well, it's all over, innit?
Hayley:	An' then there's your hair.
Kirsty:	What about it? Is it all right? The highlights are wrong, aren't they? I told her they were wrong. She took hours doing them an' I told her she's got 'em wrong.
Hayley:	No, they're fine. I just don't know anybody who's as dedicated to her hair as you are.
Kirsty:	Well, there's nothin' else worth it in life is there? I mean, shoes, clothes, hair an' piercings, that's what life is all about. It don't get no better than this.
Hayley:	Hey, Kirsty?
Kirsty:	What, Hayley?
Hayley:	Do you think there are some people what might think we were, like, a little bit shallow?
Kirsty:	Shallow? What d'ya mean?
Hayley:	Well, some people might think that dedicating your life to *EastEnders* and fingernails, or shoes, clothes, hair an' piercings was a bit, like, shallow.
Kirsty:	Oh what, like, there's anything more in life than that?
Hayley:	Well, what about love, friendship, loyalty, kindness? What about justice, equality, making people's lives better? What about spirituality, God, church? What about discovering meaning and purpose to life? What about Jesus?
Kirsty:	Well, is he fit?
Hayley:	No, you plonker, he's got a beard.
Kirsty:	Well, I'm not interested then. Face it, Hayley, we've got all in life that we shall ever need. The things we're dedicated to will never let us down.
Hayley:	Except those platform shoes you fell off.
Kirsty:	Now, don't even get me started, Hayley.

Where God is

(Two actors stand centrally)

Voice 1:   Well, good morning everybody.

Voice 2:   Good morrow to you, indeed, and a hey nonny no.

Voice 1:   A what?

Voice 2:   Sorry, just trying to be cheerful. After all, it is a day of great joy, felicitation and celebration, is it not?

Voice 1:   Indeed it is. A great day for festivities and cheer because today is ...

Voice 2:   Our church anniversary!

Voice 1:   Think of it ...

Voice 2:   Years and years of Christian work from this place ...

Voice 1:   If only these walls could talk.

Voice 2:   The stories they could tell.

Voice 1:   Within these walls babies have been baptized, couples have been married, children have been taught the faith. And then year in and year out there has been the faithful leading of worship.

Voice 2:   Come rain or shine, hailstorm or blizzard these doors have been open and people in large numbers and small have come to find God.

Voice 1:   Here they have sat and quietly prayed for guidance.

Voice 2:   Here they have come in anxiety and desperation.

Voice 1:   Here they have come to shed their tears as the dead have been buried.

Voice 2:   Here within these walls people have found the strength to carry on.

Voice 1:   They have laughed with their friends ...

Voice 2:   They have brought their offerings ...

Voice 1:   They have found God.

Voice 2:   Make no mistake – these walls can't hold God.

Voice 1:   That would be silly ...

Voice 2:   We'd certainly have a very small God.

Voice 1:   Church sized.

Voice 2:   I don't like to mention this ... but that's the kind of God some people would like.

Voice 1:   Church shaped and tiny.

Voice 2:   No … God is here. Faithfully joining with us week by week.

Voice 1:   But what we do here …

Voice 2:   All the worship, all the frantic church activity …

Voice 1:   Is only useful if it helps us to see God in other places too.

Voice 2:   The supermarket check-out queue …

Voice 1:   The office …

Voice 2:   The school …

Voice 1:   The home …

Voice 2:   The work place …

Voice 1:   EVERYWHERE!

Voice 2:   I think they get the idea.

Voice 1:   Are you sure? Because it's important.

Voice 2:   At the end of our service every week it's as if God throws us out into the world and says …

Voice 1:   *(in deep stern tones)* Thou puny human, listen to me, for I am thy God.

Voice 2:   What are you doing?

Voice 1:   Talking like God.

Voice 2:   You fool. God says, 'Go out. Go on. Out into the world with all of its joys and wonder and problems and pain. Go and be my people out there.'

Voice 1:   Help people who need help.

Voice 2:   Cry with people when they weep.

Voice 1:   And tell people how much I love them.

Voice 2:   Because that's what this building is all about …

Voice 1:   Helping us to live as God's people in the world, and to share the love of Jesus with everyone.

Voice 2:   And if it isn't doing that …

Voice 1:   Then what is it doing? … In Jesus' name …

Voice 2:   Amen.

Sharon and Michelle on music

(Michelle is seated, enter Sharon)

Sharon: Here, Michelle, get us a pint of shandy will ya, it's been one of them days.

Michelle: One of *what* days?

Sharon: You know.

Michelle: I don't think I do.

Sharon: Y'know – one of *them* days.

Michelle: Oh, your Damian's not been acting up again, has he?

Sharon: If only he would … at least it would show that there's some signs of life there. No, all he does is sit and watch the darts, drink lager and eat vindaloos from Arthur's Curry House.

Michelle: That's a lethal combination.

Sharon: You're telling me. It's – 'pass me the remote, love', or 'just get us another six pack out the fridge, love', or 'open that bag of crisps for me will ya, love?'. He's driving me mad.

Michelle: It sounds like it.

Sharon: I tell ya, if I hadn't come out of the house when I did, I'd have done him an injury.

Michelle: Well, you sit there – I'll go an' get your drink, an' I'll put something nice an' soothing on the jukebox.

Sharon: Ah, that'd be nice.

Michelle: 'Cos, like, music hath charms to soothe the savage beast, dunnit?

Sharon: It has what?

Michelle: I dunno. It's something my granny used to say.

Sharon: What, the one who's still doing time in prison for armed robbery?

Michelle: That's the one. She's a sweetie. She used to rock me in her arms an' say to me in her suspiciously deep voice, 'Music hath charms to soothe the savage beast.'

Sharon: An' what did she mean by that?

Michelle: Y'know, I'm not really sure. But think of where the world would be without music, eh?

Sharon: Cor, it doesn't bear thinking about.

Michelle: *(pause – thinking)* There'd be no Eurovision Song Contest.

Sharon: There you are. Nothing to listen to in shopping centres and super-markets.

Michelle: It lifts us up when we're down.

Sharon: Soothes us when we're afraid.

Michelle: It's wonderful music innit, really?

Sharon: Yeah, everything from the latest great manufactured pop band ...

Michelle: To that really fat guy what sings on the telly.

Sharon: You know, Michelle ... I love music.

Michelle: An' I do too, Sharon. You know what Rodney Simpkins says?

Sharon: What, Rodney the Christian down in Packing? Why d'you always have to bring him into it?

Michelle: I just thought what he had to say was quite interesting, that's all.

Sharon: Okay, 'Chelle, so what did the great Rodney have to say?

Michelle: He said that music is one of God's greatest gifts to us.

Sharon: Well, he would say that ... he's, like, religious, isn't he?

Michelle: Yeah, but I can see what he means.

Sharon: Oh ... an' what's that, then?

Michelle: Well, music makes me feel things that I can't describe. It makes me feel good about life even when I'm really down. It helps me.

Sharon: And?

Michelle: Well, if God made us – perhaps music's one of the ways God speaks to us. Tells us things are going to be okay, lifts us up an' gives us hope, an' happiness.

Sharon: You've really gone off the deep end, you have. All this talk about God – you'll do yourself an injury. An' by the way – I still see no pint of shandy in front of me. Nor do I hear any soothin' sounds comin' from the jukebox. After all, 'music hath charms' you know.

Michelle: Yeah, yeah. Westlife *(or similar boy band)* comin' up.

Part of the team

(This is a conversation between an oboe and the conductor of the orchestra – the oboe sits centrally, the conductor enters)

Conductor: You wanted to see me?

Oboe: Yes, Mr Conductor, I do.

Conductor: So what's on your mind?

Oboe: How long have I been with this orchestra?

Conductor: Oh, a long time.

Oboe: Twenty-five years, Mr Conductor, twenty-five years. And in all that time, have I, your top oboe, asked for anything?

Conductor: No, I can't say that you have.

Oboe: Good, I just wanted to clarify that. Because it's time that my true importance was recognized.

Conductor: But I think you're very important.

Oboe: You know that, Mr Conductor, and I know that, it's just that I think it could be made more obvious to all the other instruments. After all, who does everybody tune to? Me. I'm the one who sets the tone for the whole orchestra. My beautiful notes soar into the air.

Conductor: That's very poetic, oboe. How would you like your importance to be shown?

Oboe: Oh, I don't know. I've hardly thought about it really. Though I do so happen to have a little plan here of how it could be. *(produces plan)*

Conductor: Well, this is very impressive.

Oboe: Isn't it just?

Conductor: You've drawn yourself sitting on a little platform above all the other instruments.

Oboe: I have. After all, I think having violas on one side of me and flutes on the other just cramps my style. And, after all, I am the most important instrument in the orchestra. I need to be seen, I need to be heard. Without me the orchestra would be nothing. And to be honest with you I don't need any of those other has-beens.

Conductor: Don't need them?

Oboe: Not a bit of it. Who wants to hear a violin or a clarinet or a trombone, when they can hear me instead?

Conductor: But how would I see the bassoons with you sat on a little platform right in front of them?

Oboe: Oh, you don't need to see them … they can just follow what all the others are doing. And you seem, if you don't mind me saying so, to be missing the crucial point, which is that people need to see *me*. It doesn't actually matter about anything else.

Conductor: I see. There's another thing about this plan that's got me fascinated.

Oboe: Oh yes … and what's that?

Conductor: Well, there's three other oboes in the orchestra, but I only see you in this picture sat on your little platform.

Oboe: Um, yes. A little bit difficult this. But you know as well as I do that I am the best of the oboes.

Conductor: So, the others aren't going to be sat up there with you?

Oboe: No, just me.

Conductor: I see. Tell me, oboe, have you ever thought about what the other instruments would think if they heard you talking like this?

Oboe: Well, I … I …

Conductor: No, you haven't, have you? And have you even thought about how it would throw the whole sound of the orchestra out if you were sat high above everybody else?

Oboe: Well, I … I …

Conductor: An oboe can't turn round to a double bass and say, 'I don't need you', nor can a violin look at a tuba and say, 'I don't need you.' If that were to happen the orchestra would be destroyed and there would be no music at all.

Oboe: No orchestra? I didn't mean for that to happen.

Conductor: No, I know you didn't, but it's what happens when one instrument begins to think that they're more important than any other. In order for the music to take place, every instrument is important, and every instrument must play their part.

Oboe: And then there is beautiful music?

Conductor: Oh, it speaks of God … it speaks of God.

Traditional Trudy and Trendy Tina

(Two actors stand at the front)

Actor 1: Welcome, welcome, welcome, let me tell you a tale today. A tale of two people.

Actor 2: Not cities?

Actor 1: No, two people.

Actor 2: Oh, okay.

Actor 1: *(to actor 2)* And you're playing both of them.

Actor 2: I am?

Actor 1: Oh yes, it'll show how skilled you are.

Actor 2: Well, I *am* rather good.

Actor 1: There you go, you see. The first person in our little story is called Traditional Trudy.

Actor 2: *(putting on spectacles and hat)* Yes, indeed I am, indeed I am. You know, here in our church of St Botolph's in the Marsh we like everything to be done the way it has been for years and that especially goes for the hymns we sing. You know, I did once hear a hymn that had been written in 1953 that I rather liked but to be completely honest with you I'm more of an eighteenth-century woman myself. The glories of Wesley and Watts, the delights of earlier ages, Bunyan, Herbert and ... Thomas Tallis. Wonderful.

Actor 1: *(during this speech Actor 2 removes hat and glasses and picks up guitar)* And then, of course, there is the other character in our little tale. A lady who could not be more different from Traditional Trudy. She goes to the New Vine and Living Waters Church of Eternal Destiny, her name is Trendy Tina.

Actor 2: Hey, have you heard the new Hillsongs Praise Album? It's really stonkin'. Oh yes, in our church we can't really sing anything that was written more than ten years ago 'cos that would be a sign that we were a dead church, right, and that would be awful. Yeah, I mean, Kendrick's okay, but there's Matt Redman, Bowater, Bilbrough – oh yeah, it's great. And don't get me started on what's coming out of Australia, apart from smelly back-packers that is ... I could talk about them for hours.

Actor 1: You can see that there's a bit of a problem here. For Traditional Trudy could not see that there was anything good to be found in modern praise music at all.

Actor 2: It is repetitive, simplistic, it has no poetry, no deep purpose. It is played badly, sung poorly and sounds rather too much like Andrew Lloyd Webber on a very bad day indeed. I would not allow that material within ten miles of my beloved church door.

Actor 1: Strong feelings, indeed, but then, of course, Trendy Tina felt things just as strongly in completely the opposite direction.

Actor 2: Repetitive? What about chanting psalms in plainsong? I tell you, what people need today is modern music, music that's going to lift them and move them and shake them and make them feel something. I tell you, no church that sings them dead old hymns is alive and moving forward. There's just no spirit in them at all. You need to move into the twenty-first century.

Actor 1: Neither Trendy Tina nor Traditional Trudy would listen to the other person. They couldn't, you see – their ears were closed. And the fact is that both of them were wrong.

Actor 2: *(now back to herself)* They were?

Actor 1: Oh yes. Do you think God only gave inspiration to hymn writers in the 1700s or in the twenty-first century?

Actor 2: Of course not.

Actor 1: There you go. And do you think God has only inspired one kind of music and could not possibly speak through another?

Actor 2: That would be silly – you'd be limiting God.

Actor 1: There you go, you see.

Actor 2: So there's riches in both.

Actor 1: Absolutely.

Actor 2: God can speak through both.

Actor 1: Exactly.

Actor 2: So why can't they see that?

Actor 1: Now that is a question that's worth pondering. And what better way to ponder than over a nice cup of tea?

Actor 2: Lovely – two sugars please.

The mission

(Enter Dora and Nora talking)

Dora: So, what did you make of that then, Nora?

Nora: Shocking, that's what I thought of it, Dora, shocking.

Dora: Well, I must admit I'd find it difficult to do.

Nora: Well, of course you would, Dora dear – as would I. When the vicar invited us to this meeting tonight I thought it would be an overdue opportunity to talk about the mess the Mums and Tots group leave the hall in.

Dora: I certainly didn't think that he'd want to talk to us about the church doing a mission.

Nora: Expecting us to go out and speak about our faith! To total strangers as well. The man must be off his rocker. I haven't talked about religion in public since 1972 when our Jane was baptized, and even then I only did it under protest. It's not that I didn't want to bring Jane up in a Christian home – although her recent dabbling with animal rights activists threatens to go too far – it's just that I don't expect to talk about it in front of invited guests.

Dora: I think he said he wanted us to go around and knock on people's doors, deliver leaflets and such like. At least, I think that's what he wanted. I must admit I came over all dizzy when he started talking about it. I thought I might be having one of me turns so I went outside to take some air.

Nora: You did absolutely the right thing. Talking about God and Jesus, inviting people to church, it's just not done.

Dora: It would be nice to see more people in church though, wouldn't it, Nora?

Nora: Well, of course it would, but we ring the church bells loud and long each Sunday morning, don't we? What more does the vicar want?

Dora: I would like to have more confidence in my faith, you know. Perhaps this is the way to do it.

Nora: Look, Dora, I have absolutely no doubts about my ability to draw in new members. Why, I single-handedly enlisted fifteen new members into the National Trust last year. They said that I was close to being certified.

Dora: Don't you mean certificated?

Nora: Do try not to tell me what I do and do not mean, dear. The point is that I can get people to join things if I want to.

Dora: So don't you like the church, then? Don't you think it's worth joining?

Nora: I dare say it is, Dora, but it's just not a very British thing to do now, is it?

Dora: To do what?

Nora: Why, talk about Jesus, of course. People will think we're religious nutters or something, not members of the parish church with a place to uphold in the community.

Dora: But the vicar said that every generation of Christians has the potential to be the last.

Nora: Oh, stuff and nonsense, and anyway, as long as the church is there to hold my funeral in, what do I care?

Dora: So we're against this idea of a mission, are we?

Nora: Completely and utterly.

Dora: Even though the most natural thing to want to do with good news is to share it.

Nora: Er ... quite.

Dora: And even though Jesus asked us to.

Nora: Now, Dora, you're just being difficult. I've got better things to do with my time than to share life-saving good news of salvation. Come along.

Little Snoring

(Revd Stephen Parker is onstage, enter Gemima)

Stephen: Ah, good morning, you must be Gemima.

Gemima: Indeed I am, Revd Parker.

Stephen: Oh, please, call me Stephen.

Gemima: Okay, Steve, that's great. We here at Mission Advice and Enabling Global and International exist to meet the needs of churches to spread the Good News.

Stephen: Wonderful, that's just what we're looking for.

Gemima: Let's get right down to it. We envisage a high-tech, maximum impact, strategically targeted mission to the people of your community. We've done an in-depth assessment of the socio-economic trends and the customer profiles of the area and here's our report. *(takes out huge pile of papers)*

Stephen: Gracious!

Gemima: We envisage an initial mail-shot of the entire community, extensive telephone canvassing, detailed work with focus groups, a glossy prospectus, five or six major events, a parade, the hiring of a big-name evangelist, digital projectors, cinema surround-sound, display screens, the works.

Stephen: But Little Snoring in-the-Marsh only has a population of 370.

Gemima: And do these people not deserve to be wowed with technology, Steve?

Stephen: Well, it's not that ...

Gemima: I know, it's the cost implications, isn't it? Spreading the gospel in this way doesn't come cheap. We've got publicity material to design and produce, equipment to hire, top professionals to engage. We were thinking in the region of £47,000.

Stephen: What? Have you seen the congregation here?

Gemima: Well, I staked out the church last Sunday from inside the pub across the road.

Stephen: I've got no more than fifteen in the congregation, all of them over seventy years old. Now, don't get me wrong, they're eager to spread the gospel, willing to get involved, they just need some help in giving them the confidence to do it.

Gemima: And they'll have all the confidence that 47k will buy them, Steve.

Stephen: But all this talk of digital projectors, glossy documentation, parades – this is a rural village, Gemima, we don't need any of that.

Gemima: Oh, but we do, Steve. Modern-day evangelism demands it, the people of Little Snoring in-the-Marsh demand it. More importantly, our highly paid researchers say that it's necessary.

Stephen: And where did your highly paid researchers do their research?

Gemima: Kensington, Knightsbridge and Chelsea.

Stephen: Well, that's representative.

Gemima: Look, these are highly paid professionals – I think we can trust their judgements.

Stephen: About Kensington, Knightsbridge and Chelsea, yes – but this is a rural community which needs a little bit of confidence boosting. What works in one place isn't going to work in another – I'd have thought even your highly paid professionals could have told you that.

Gemima: So you're telling me that each mission, each piece of evangelism has to take into account what's possible and appropriate in the local community?

Stephen: That's about it, yes.

Gemima: What a novel idea; totally bonkers, of course, but novel. Well, thank you for your time, Revd Parker, it was a pleasure. I'll send you my consultancy bill in the post. *(she sweeps out quickly)*

Stephen: But ...

How lovely!

(Enter Princesses Anastasia and Gwendolyn)

Gwendolyn: Do you know what?

Anastasia: I bet you'll never guess!

Gwendolyn: No, I bet you never will.

Anastasia: Gwendolyn – stunning Gwendolyn – and I are sisters!

Gwendolyn: Yes indeed, indeed, beauteous Anastasia and I are sisters!

Anastasia: Greetings, lovely Gwendolyn!

Gwendolyn: Salutations, gorgeous Anastasia!

Anastasia: Do you know what, dazzling sister Gwendolyn?

Gwendolyn: I don't think I do, darling sister Anastasia.

Anastasia: My favourite day of the whole year, apart from all the days when we have glittering balls and sumptuous parties, is here.

Gwendolyn: Excuse me for butting in, wonderful sister Anastasia, but we have glittering balls and sumptuous parties *every* day of the year.

Anastasia: So we do! But still – today is a day for extravagant rejoicing and much merry-making.

Gwendolyn: And why is that?

Anastasia: Well, you know as well as I do, glorious sister Gwendolyn, that our horrid relations, the obnoxious Prince Roderick and the unspeakable Princess Celia, have made our lives a misery all summer.

Gwendolyn: Oh they have, they have. They are perfectly disgusting little children.

Anastasia: With their incessant chatter.

Gwendolyn: And their constant desire to be entertained.

Anastasia: Well, that is all coming to an end.

Gwendolyn: Now, please, do not tease me, delectable sister Anastasia, for this is news that is too good to be true.

Anastasia: But it is true, dearest sister Gwendolyn, for on Monday the two little brats who have destroyed the peace of our lives all summer are to return to school.

Gwendolyn: You mean the new school year is here already? What heady news is this!

Anastasia: Quite so. But there is one thing that is puzzling me, magnificent sister Gwendolyn.

Gwendolyn: And what is that, outstanding sister Anastasia?

Anastasia: When I spoke to Roderick and Celia about the forthcoming school year, hoping that I could enjoy their misery at the thought of returning to that place of torment, I was struck, instead, by how happy the thought of returning made them.

Gwendolyn: That is, indeed, most odd. I would have thought they should be loathing the thought of going back. All of that expansion of their minds with knowledge.

Anastasia: All of those new ideas that you have to wrestle with.

Gwendolyn: All of that interacting with other people.

Anastasia: Concerts to be performed.

Gwendolyn: Poetry to be recited.

Anastasia: A whole world to be discovered. How perfectly horrid.

Gwendolyn: Anybody would think that God had given us minds to be expanded and exercised.

Anastasia: Quite so. But as I say, the thought of all of that seemed to excite and enthuse Roderick and Celia immensely. And when I said I assumed that they would miss their darling relations here in the castle – do you know what Prince Roderick said?

Gwendolyn: No, but I feel sure that you will tell me.

Anastasia: He said they had been bored here all summer, that we were no fun to be with, and that he was looking forward to all the excitement of being back at school.

Gwendolyn: Why, that ungrateful little toad! If God had meant us to enjoy learning, he wouldn't have given us daytime television.

Anastasia: That is precisely what I said, entrancing sister Gwendolyn.

Gwendolyn: Well, I am determined not to trouble my mind about it anymore.

Anastasia: A mind which remains almost pristine in the sense that it has never been troubled with a thought or an idea in its entire life.

Gwendolyn: And I fully intend to keep it so. School ... pah!

Anastasia: How eloquently put ... pah!

Gwendolyn: I am off to do absolutely nothing of any use with my mind all day. Are you coming, sublime sister Anastasia?

Anastasia: Lead the way, radiant sister Gwendolyn.

If only

(Raphael sits centrally, enter Gabriel)

Gabriel: 'Morning, Raphael.

Raphael: 'Morning, Gabriel.

Gabriel: Fancy an angel cake?

Raphael: No, but if you've got any Angel Delight left I'll have that.

Gabriel: It's a tough life being an angel, isn't it?

Raphael: People have no idea.

Gabriel: Flitting this way and that.

Raphael: Always about our master's business.

Gabriel: So, before you go off duty is there anything I should know about?

Raphael: Actually, yes. I've got a rather sad message come in on the prayer request desk overnight.

Gabriel: Oh yeah, what's that, then?

Raphael: A nine-year-old girl in Manchester upset because she's getting picked on at school.

Gabriel: I hate it when children do that.

Raphael: Let's be honest, the adults aren't much better.

Gabriel: I know, but somehow it always seems worse when it's a kid.

Raphael: Well, this one's pretty upset. Seems people have been calling her names, pushing and kicking her – generally making her life a bit of a misery.

Gabriel: This is tempting me to be not very angelic at all.

Raphael: I know. And it gets worse.

Gabriel: How can it get any worse than that?

Raphael: It's the reason they're doing it.

Gabriel: Which is?

Raphael: She's black, they're white.

Gabriel: And these kids are doing this to her – making her life a misery just because she's a different colour from them?

Raphael: It would appear so.

Gabriel: I can't believe it! What is going on in the heads of these people? Have they any idea how precious they are? How loved they are?

Raphael: If they had they wouldn't be doing this.

Gabriel: Oooh, let me get down there, I'll show them. I'll say I thought we'd brought back the whole vengeful, wrathful God thing, just for a moment. Just let me at them.

Raphael: Slow down, Gabriel. Calm down.

Gabriel: But how dare they treat part of God's creation like that?

Raphael: I know – sometimes I think it would be better if humans were all coffee coloured, then we wouldn't have any of this trouble.

Gabriel: Don't you believe it – they'd just pick on some other difference to have a go at. So what's this little girl's name?

Raphael: Melissa. Here's the prayer request. *(hands over a piece of paper)*

Gabriel: Oh, I can feel the sadness, the faith, the love, the heartache. It's all here. And what a tremendous faith.

Raphael: She's even asked for them to be forgiven.

Gabriel: Right – I'm going down there. Melissa is about to have a close encounter of an angelic kind.

Raphael: You taking the choir?

Gabriel: I just might do, actually. Cheer her up a bit.

Raphael: Does the choir of angels perform rap and hip-hop?

Gabriel: You hum it, son, and I'll play it. I'm just amazed at how people can treat each other.

Raphael: You and me both, Gabriel. Have a nice trip.

Gabriel: I will – Melissa is about to discover how special she really is.

Dahlias and weeds

(Two actors walk to the front)

Actor 1: *(big and expansive)* Welcome to Harvest Festival. I am a glorious dahlia.

Actor 2: *(rather shamefaced)* And I'm a little weed.

Actor 1: See, everybody, look at my glorious colour, my wonderful petals.

Actor 2: I'm a dandelion and I'm yellow.

Actor 1: I know I'm slightly difficult to grow but look at how beautiful I am.

Actor 2: I get everywhere, I do. In your lawn, between cracks in the pavement, in your guttering ... sorry about that. I'm very persistent.

Actor 1: Yes, persistence is one thing, but who would want to put you in a harvest display? I mean, why are you even here? I'm rare and slightly fragile, difficult to grow but with a blaze of colour.

Actor 2: Yes, I can see that. You're very beautiful.

Actor 1: And you, on the other hand ... well, look at you. You're tough as old boots. What happened the last time somebody tried to dig you up?

Actor 2: I just came right on back.

Actor 1: Exactly – do you have any idea how frustrating you are? How difficult your roots are to dig up?

Actor 2: *(chuckling)* I *am* a little obstinate.

Actor 1: Obstinate? Obstinate? That's putting it mildly. Just when gardeners think they've dug deep enough, that they've managed to lever out the whole of your root system ...

Actor 2: I go and prove them wrong. I'm tough that way.

Actor 1: I'm so special and you're so ordinary.

Actor 2: Yes, I know.

Actor 1: So do you really think you ought to be here at all? In this harvest display?

Actor 2:   Well, I'm not sure – but the preacher said I had pride of place.

Actor 1:   What? How dare she? Pride of place? What an affront! I've never in all my born days …

Actor 2:   No, I've never, either … but the preacher said I was truly special … a picture, she said.

Actor 1:   A picture? How could she be so blind? I mean, a van Gogh, that's a picture, a Renoir, a Gainsborough … but you? You're a weed, for goodness sake!

Actor 2:   Yes, well, the preacher said I was a picture of faith. A faith that's tough and doesn't give up, a faith that's hardy and grows in the most difficult places, a faith that's ordinary and everyday and gets everywhere. A faith that can't be destroyed but has deep roots that are impossible to destroy. She said if only every Christian could have a faith like mine rather than …

Actor 1:   Rather than what? Come, come, I demand to know!

Actor 2:   Rather than being an over-dramatic, here-one-day-gone-the-next, self-important glory seeker like some dahlias.

Actor 1:   I … I … this is outrageous! For once I'm lost for words! How could they? I am a dahlia! That's a very important flower, you know. This is not the end of this little event, you know … oh no, I'm off to a higher authority. Self-important? Moi? I'm off to find Alan Titchmarsh. *(stalks off)*

Actor 2:   So, the question is … what kind of faith do you have? Oh, and sorry about my seeds. I know … they spread everywhere, don't they?

A tale of two seeds

(The first actor runs on, as if flying through the air having been thrown)

Seed 1: I fly through the air, with the greatest of ease … watch out below, ready or not, here I come. Geronimo! *(lands and looks around)* So, let's see where I've landed. *(treads the ground)* Hmm, not bad. Not bad at all. In fact it's very good. Nice bit of mulch, I could do quite well here. Bit of rain, bit of sunshine and Bob's your uncle. *(addresses audience)* You see, you can never be quite sure. I mean, I know the farmer tries his best to throw you into good soil, but when you're a seed life's a bit of a lottery. My pal Joey, the carrot seed, he got tossed a bit too far – flew over the edge of the field boundary, fell down a motorway bank on to the M6 and was picked up by an errant breeze which deposited him on a truck headed for Strathclyde. Never seen again. *(second seed appears running on – lands a little way from the first)*

Seed 2: Oo-er, here I come. Oooh, I never liked flying. Get out the way! *(lands)* Ouch. You know, they could have been more careful. I don't think that was very good seed-spreading at all. I mean a great big hand just digs down in the bag and throws you through the air. What kind of seed management is that? *(shouts up at farmer)* Deploy your seed resources in a more sensible manner next time, please. *(looks around)* Now, where am I?

Seed 1: *(waves)* Coo-ee! Hello.

Seed 2: Oh, hello. Have you just experienced the ultimate in economy air travel too?

Seed 1: I have, yes. But at least the ground's good. Nice soft, rich soil – it's going to be great. How's yours?

Seed 2: What, the soil you mean? I don't know, I haven't had time to look yet. *(treads on ground)* Wait a minute, I thought you said this soil was good?

Seed 1: Well mine is … it's lovely.

Seed 2: This is hard, it's like rock. *(stamps)* No, not 'like' rock, it *is* rock. Is this some kind of joke? How am I meant to grow on this?

Seed 1: With difficulty I'd have thought.

Seed 2: *(heavy with sarcasm)* No … you don't say.

Seed 1: There's no need to be sarcastic.

Seed 2:   I'm sorry, but you're not the one who's going to get burnt up and withered by the sun in the next ten minutes.

Seed 1:   Yes, sorry, I see your point.

Seed 2:   Well, I wish I could see the point.

Seed 1:   What do you mean?

Seed 2:   Well, what's the point of my life? I'm just as good a seed as you. I've got just as much right to grow and develop. And you get to dig down in lovely rich soil and I get burned up on a rock. What is the point of my life?

Seed 1:   Look, we're here to deliver an important lesson, aren't we?

Seed 2:   We are?

Seed 1:   Yes – we're in a parable.

Seed 2:   What's that?

Seed 1:   It's a story with a hidden meaning.

Seed 2:   So before I'm burned to a crisp, am I permitted to know what the hidden meaning of this story is?

Seed 1:   Oh yes. We are the word of God, you see.

Seed 2:   So we're not seeds at all?

Seed 1:   Do I look like a seed to you?

Seed 2:   Come to think of it, I've never seen a seed with clothes and hair and teeth.

Seed 1:   So ... the word of God gets sown but people have all kinds of different reactions to it.

Seed 2:   Represented by these different kinds of soil?

Seed 1:   Exactly.

Seed 2:   So how come you get the jolly, warm wet mulch reception and I get the rocky road?

Seed 1:   Luck of the draw, I guess.

Seed 2:   Great. Still, *you'll* have a great harvest.

Seed 1:   I will. But there's one more problem for you.

Seed 2:   What's that?

Seed 1:   That shadow up there? It's a bird.

Seed 2:   Argghh!

What does it mean?

(Two actors sit centrally)

Gemma: Look, I can't come Thursday, I've got to go to the school harvest festival.

Kate: *(excited)* Oh, how sweet! Can I come?

Gemma: No, you can't – he's nervous enough as it is.

Kate: Oh go on! Lots of five-year-olds dressed up as tins of baked beans and cauliflowers; it'll be great!

Gemma: Yeah, well, that's why he's nervous. He's the 'third beetroot' – it's a lot of responsibility – the last thing he needs is you waving at him like some maniac on the front row.

Kate: Oh, but I used to love harvest festivals, *(sings)* 'All things bright and beautiful ...'

Gemma: Yes, thank you, that's quite enough of that.

Kate: It is a bit weird though, isn't it?

Gemma: What?

Kate: Singing about fields of golden corn ripening in the sun.

Gemma: So?

Kate: We live in Peckham. You're going to the school on the bus. You buy your food at Sainsbury's. When was the last time you saw a field of amber grain?

Gemma: Last year when I was on holiday ... but that's not the point.

Kate: So what is the point?

Gemma: It's traditional, isn't it?

Kate: And that makes it right, does it?

Gemma: Look, Kate, don't confuse me with the facts – since when have you ever used logic?

Kate: I just think it's interesting. I mean, here we are, we have no connection with the harvest at all. We don't grow anything, we don't harvest food, we go down the shops once a week. I work in an office where you can't even see the world outside. What kind of connection to the great change of the seasons is that?

Gemma: All right, all right, you've made your point. So what would *you* have us do?

Kate: I dunno.

Gemma: Oh well, that's really useful.

Kate: We could spend some time thinking about what harvest means to us.

Gemma: And that would mean?

Kate: Well – if we were looking at the harvest of our lives what would it be? Satisfied customers from the call centre? A good plumbing job done? Being cheerful with people when you meet them on the bus?

Gemma: But that's hardly about food, is it?

Kate: No, but it is saying to God – here are the things that are a harvest of *our* lives – the things that *we* do – thank you for helping us to do all these things.

Gemma: And you think that would work?

Kate: Why not? I mean, I'm not saying replace all the fruit and veg – it is good to say 'thank you' for food, but why not, as well as all that, have Lenny from the garage bring in a set of tools? Jane could bring in her laptop, Bruce could bring in his tachometer and Violet could bring her school crossing uniform. All of that is the harvest of our lives – why don't we offer all of it?

Gemma: I suppose at least then we'd be offering personal things. Things that mean something to us.

Kate: Exactly ... it'd be great. So what do you think?

Gemma: I think it's worth bringing up – asking what other people think. After all, when do we get to offer the harvest that God has given to *us*?

Kate: Quite right. And as a reward for this stupendously brilliant idea, you're going to invite me to your son's lovely school harvest festival on Thursday, aren't you?

Gemma: Not in a million years ... 'bye Kate. *(she exits)*

Kate: *(following)* Oh come on, Gemma, I'd be really good ... *Please*?

Two verses

(Two people stand centrally)

One: You'll never guess this.

Two: No, we bet you never will.

One: But my colleague and I are ...

Two: Bible verses.

One: Yes, Bible verses.

Two: I am Micah, Chapter 6 verse 8, depending on your translation, 'The Lord has told you mortals what is good, and what it is that the Lord requires of you: only to act justly, to love loyalty, to walk humbly with your God.'

One: And I am Philippians Chapter 3 verse 14, again depending on your translation, 'I press towards the finishing line, to win the heavenly prize to which God has called me in Christ Jesus.'

Two: Now we'd be the first to say it's important to read the verses around us.

One: Of course it is. We're part of complete documents.

Two: Complex arguments.

One: But being a verse in the Bible is the most wonderful thing.

Two: We have so much power.

One: You wouldn't believe it, would you?

Two: Just a few words.

One: A few squiggles of ink on a piece of paper.

Two: But we have the power to change people's lives completely.

One: I remember back in 1733. Somebody read me and I could suddenly feel the page getting moist. I looked up and tears were falling on the paper. The person who was reading me was anxious, lonely, depressed, almost ready to give up on life. And reading me turned his life around. He found hope, joy, peace, courage and strength to carry on. It was incredible.

Two: Back in 1847 a preacher used me as a text for his sermon. He preached powerfully on my words and thirty-four people that night gave their lives to Christ. Each one of those people read me in years to come and found new levels of comfort and strength.

One: In 1915 I was read in a trench in World War I. It was a pretty battered Bible, muddy and well worn, but I helped a young man to get through another night of hell on earth.

Two: In 2004 I was downloaded from the internet for a digitally projected presentation that a preacher was using in a piece of worship. She made children smile and gave them something to remember for the week to come.

One: I'm afraid also in 2004 I was in rather too many Bibles that sat on bookshelves, never taken down, never opened, just gathering dust. How can God help people through me if they never read me?

Two: We need to be studied, thought about, applied, discussed.

One: What good can we ever do to anybody if we're sat up on a shelf with the other reference books, just in case there's a clue in a crossword we might be able to help with?

Two: The good news is, though, we are selling as well as ever.

One: We are in more languages than ever before.

Two: And in more formats.

One: We are digital.

Two: Downloadable.

One: In comic book form.

Two: In drama.

One: It's actually a very exciting time for us.

Two: In all kinds of ways we are reaching more people in more ways than ever.

One: Which means that God is able to reach out through us to touch the lives of more people than ever.

Two: And *that* is wonderful.

One: And powerful.

Two: And amazing.

One: And glorious.

Two: And brilliant.

One: The end.

Two: Well, in fact, it's just the beginning.

One world

(Two actors stand centrally)

One: Me and my mate are here today ...

Two: Yes, my chum and I are present now ...

One: To tell you something of vital importance ...

Two: Of supreme vitalness.

One: 'Vitalness'?

Two: Well, you were on a roll and I didn't want to let you down.

One: But 'vitalness' isn't even a word.

Two: Don't you think I don't know that? I was in a hurry, I was flustered, and by the way ...

One: What is it?

Two: *(motioning to congregation)* They're still watching us.

One: Oh ... yes, of course. Anyway, we're here to tell you something really ...

Two: Stunningly ...

One: Important.

Two: The world we live on ...

One: That world is one.

Two: It sounds simple, doesn't it?

One: We live on one world.

Two: Not two.

One: Not three.

Two: But one.

One: Except for my cousin Vera.

Two: Oh yes, I always said she was on another planet.

One: And indeed she is.

Two: But apart from cousin Vera, we live on one world.

One: And we are all connected to each other.

Two: *(intoning grandly)* In the great circle of life.

One: Yes ... very good.

Two: Now, there's a problem here.

One: There certainly is, because we are surrounded by people every day.

Two: Every minute of every day ...

One: Telling us how divided the world is.

Two: And, indeed, the world is a very divided place.

One: Rich and poor ...

Two: North and south ...

One: Black and white ...

Two: Young and old ...

One: East and west ...

Two: Male and female ...

One: You name it, there's a division for it.

Two: The problem is, we hear and see so much about divisions ...

One: We allow those divisions to rule our lives.

Two: To throw up great walls between us. *(mimes building a wall between them)*

One: Walls that are pretty difficult to tear down. *(mimes pulling it down)*

Two: I suppose at the end of the day ...

One: When all is said and done ...

Two: It's all about what we want to define us.

One: To shape who we are.

Two: Do we want to be moulded and formed by the things that divide us?

One: 'I'm richer than you are.'

Two: 'I'm a woman, therefore I can multi-task, and you can't.'

One: Or do we want to get rid of all that divisive nonsense and begin to understand that we are all ...

Two: Even his cousin Vera ...

One: Part of one beautiful ...

Two: Wonderful ...

One: Glorious ...

Two: Stunning world.

One: Created and loved by God.

Two: One world.

One: One human family.

Two: One God.

One: World without end.

Two: Amen.

The supermarket

(Tracy sits at a supermarket check-out. Vera approaches with shopping – all the props can be imaginary or real)

Tracy: 'Morning.

Vera: 'Morning. *(opening shopping bag)*

Tracy: Would you like anybody to pack for you?

Vera: No thanks.

Tracy: Any cash back?

Vera: No thanks.

Tracy: Reward points?

Vera: *(increasingly testy)* No.

Tracy: Help to take your shopping to the car?

Vera: No.

Tracy: Petrol coupons?

Vera: NO! ... thank you.

Tracy: Only trying to help. *(starts emptying the basket)* Ooh, look at this!

Vera: Look at what?

Tracy: Nothing.

Vera: What do you mean, 'nothing'?

Tracy: Well, we're told not to engage testy customers in witty banter or conversation.

Vera: Are you?

Tracy: Yes, it's still interesting though, isn't it?

Vera: What is?

Tracy: Well, look at this – it's like you've got the whole world in a basket here.

Vera: I have?

Tracy: Absolutely. Look here, you've got apples from South Africa, tea from Sri Lanka, coffee from Columbia, bananas from Barbados, rice from India, cranberry juice from the United States, chocolate with cocoa from Ghana. You've got olive oil from Italy, cheese from France and pork from good old British pigs.

Vera: *(interested despite herself)* Have I?

Tracy: Oh, absolutely. You see those socks you've bought? They were made up in China, you've got tuna from the Seychelles, pineapple chunks from Paraguay, and those knickers you've got were made in Indonesia.

Vera: That is quite impressive, actually.

Tracy: It is wonderful, isn't it? How we're all dependent on each other, how your life wouldn't be the same without people from all over the world doing their little part.

Vera: I suppose you're right.

Tracy: I know I am, dear. This supermarket's like your very own neighbourhood United Nations – except we give reward points.

Vera: I'd not really even thought about it before.

Tracy: No, not a lot of people have, which is part of the point of this extremely well-acted sketch. The fact is that we are interdependent.

Vera: Part of one world with access to all the wonderful things that the world has to offer.

Tracy: Which includes ostrich meat from the exotic environs of Hemel Hempstead.

Vera: I can't help feeling we're the lucky ones, though.

Tracy: Oh, you have no idea. People working all hours for low pay. No health care, no education.

Vera: It doesn't feel like we're part of the same planet at all sometimes.

Tracy: But that's just the problem, we really don't think about the rest of the world enough ... do we, dear?

Vera: I ought to take more notice. Learn about what's going on right underneath my nose and care about it too.

Tracy: Me and you both, love. One world? Doesn't seem like it sometimes. That'll be £44.26, please.

Responsibility

(Camilla sits in an upmarket coffee shop – enter McKenna)

Camilla: Darling McKenna, how are you?

McKenna: Oh Camilla, darling, I'm positively wretched. How are you?

Camilla: Hideous, darling.

McKenna: So what would you like?

Camilla: Well, *(reading menu)* there's cappuccino, espresso, ristretto, latte, filter or mochaccino.

McKenna: *(also reading)* ... topped off with whipped cream, marshmallows, real chocolate shavings, vanilla, caramel, cinnamon, almond or hazelnut and ginger.

Camilla: Not much of a selection is it, darling?

McKenna: Positively primeval. What about the teas?

Camilla: Well, they've got English breakfast, Earl Grey, Assam, Darjeeling, camomile, peppermint, mixed fruit, lemon verbena, Japanese green tea, silver jasmine or china white.

McKenna: Is that it?

Camilla: 'Fraid so. *(looking at menu again)* Oh no, wait a minute, there's a little note right at the bottom of the menu.

McKenna: I hate little notes, they're always so furtive.

Camilla: Absolutely, darling. I was only saying to Lucinda the other day, I hate furtive little notes.

McKenna: So what does the little note on the menu say?

Camilla: 'Fair Trade Teas and Coffees also available.'

McKenna: Fair Trade ... what's that?

Camilla: Isn't that where they pay the little people who grow the tea and coffee a fair wage for their labours?

McKenna: Don't they get a fair wage already?

Camilla: Apparently not, darling.

McKenna: So they don't have enough to buy Gucci handbags and Armani accessories?

Camilla: I would suppose not.

McKenna: Well, that's frightful, but what's it got to do with me?

Camilla: I suppose it depends on whether you feel responsible or not, darling, doesn't it?

McKenna: Oh, I gave up on responsibility as a bad idea years ago.

Camilla: Ditto, darling – if people the other side of the world don't have enough money to live on what's it got to do with me?

McKenna: Quite – all we do is drink the tea and coffee they make. And, anyway, the real question, darling, has yet to be asked.

Camilla: Will this fair trade thingy go with our designer lifestyles? I mean, it would have to be outrageously trendy and very chic for me to be seen within a hundred miles of it.

McKenna: Moi aussi, darling. Is it what the smartest people are doing?

Camilla: You know, it's hard to get upset over what's happening at the end of my street in Knightsbridge, let alone in India or Brazil.

McKenna: After all, my lifestyle doesn't have anything to do with anybody but me and my accountant.

Camilla: Responsibility for how other people live is not my thing.

McKenna: Just because we live on the same planet, doesn't mean I have to worry about them.

Camilla: So let's just drink our tea, eat our chocolate, and enjoy our apricot pastries.

McKenna: After all, we don't rely on the rest of the world at all.

Camilla: Do we?

The museum

(The Curator and visitor enter – obviously on a guided tour)

Curator: Welcome, everybody, welcome. Come into The Museum of Human Frailty. In this collection we have brought together artefacts that show how silly, vain, greedy and violent human beings can be.

Visitor: It sounds fascinating.

Curator: Madam, you have no idea. Here we have a genuine diamond-encrusted designer necklace worn by an actress to a ceremony called the 'Oscars' in 2002. It cost £4 million. The day after the ceremony the very same actress made a statement about how important the issue of world poverty was to her.

Visitor: I can hardly believe it.

Curator: I know, I know. From where we stand in the twenty-second century it does sound rather bizarre, but then so does the TV show *Pop Idol*.

Visitor: Oh, now, I've heard about this. Grasping, self-absorbed young people would compete against each other singing old songs badly because they thought that fame was important.

Curator: Exactly. And in our collection we have a range of false smiles and hair-care products used on the show. But the most important part of our display here in the museum is our 'War Room'.

Visitor: Oh, of course, they still went to war with each other, didn't they?

Curator: Oh yes. World peace was only a distant dream, hoped for and prayed for by a group of brave and courageous individuals. This was an age of fear and hatred, of land-mines and anthrax threats, of a massive arms trade and children with guns.

Visitor: It sounds awful.

Curator: It was. We have in our collection the most horrific selection of devices used to inflict unimaginable pain and suffering, damaging life in every way possible. And, unfortunately, we also have photos to prove they were used.

Visitor: And yet throughout this terrible period there were people who never lost hope. People continued to work and pray for peace.

Curator: Indeed, and as we know now, their prayers and actions were crucial to the progress that eventually took place.

Visitor: It's just as well they didn't give up.

Curator: Even though they must have wondered whether they were making any headway at all sometimes.

Visitor: Well, this certainly sounds a fascinating collection – I'll have a look round if that's okay.

Curator: Of course it is. It's absolutely vital that we don't let memories like this fade away. We really must remember how barbaric and inhuman people have been to each other at times. And how important continued prayer is. But don't forget that on the third floor we also have our ultimate testament to the limits of human endurance. We have the complete collection of the works of that titan of twentieth-century entertainment, Des O'Connor.

Visitor: Oooh, it sounds lovely.

Curator: You won't say that when you've heard it.

Rosie and Jack

(Two actors – one male, one female – Rosie sits to one side, Jack stands separately)

Jack: And I heard the sound of crows squawking in the morning mist ...

Rosie: *(speaking to the audience)* I had such fond memories of all of them – they were *my* boys, you see. I can hardly believe it.

Jack: And the crack of shells shattered the peace ...

Rosie: I was so proud of them. I know it's silly. But I was like their mother, wasn't I? Well, it stands to reason, doesn't it? A boarding school – them spending most of their lives here. They saw more of me than their mums and dads.

Jack: And the splatter of mud as it flew through the air ...

Rosie: They used to come to me to darn their socks. And when they first arrived and were a bit homesick they'd pop in and I'd have a pot of tea on and they'd tell me all sorts. 'Matron,' they'd say, 'I can tell you anything.'

Jack: The whistle of bullets flying through the air ...

Rosie: And they've gone on to great things, some of my boys. Engineers and doctors, businessmen and lawyers ... great things. And then the war came.

Jack: The sound of whimpers and screams cutting through the mist ...

Rosie: And they were so keen to join up, most of them. 'To serve King and country; that must be the greatest honour of all,' they'd say. I'd say, 'It's 1914, we're in the modern world now – that just means they're always coming up with new and better ways to kill young lads.' And they'd say, 'Oh matron, don't be so daft, we'll be home for Christmas.' ... I knew they wouldn't be.

Jack: The shouts of men, clambering over the top ...

Rosie: It was a glorious summer that year. June was wonderful, and on Wednesday afternoons they had sport and I'd sneak out and watch them playing cricket in a blaze of summer sunshine. They looked wonderful in their cricketing whites, not a care in the world, celebrating life. It was good to be alive and watching them. All of that goodness, all of that joy and potential and wonder. They'd come in for tea and scoff platefuls of my sandwiches and drink lemonade. Seventeen years old they were – the whole of life stretching out before them.

Jack: The squelch of boots sinking into wet mud …

Rosie: And as I sat there on that glorious afternoon watching them in the summer haze, laughing and joking and enjoying life, I suddenly felt cold, and a shiver ran down my back.

Jack: We were frightened, you see, and young, so young.

Rosie: Jack Rutherford went out in the August. I'd watched him play cricket a month before and by September he was in the front line stuck in some God-forsaken trench somewhere I'd never heard of. And that's where he died. It was October. They brought his body back and we buried him in the graveyard. He wasn't the first and he wasn't going to be the last. But he was one of my boys and that … well, it meant something. I'll never forget the look on his mother's face at the funeral. Frightening, like all the life had been drained out of her. I couldn't believe it. I'd watched him play cricket just three months before. He had so much to offer, so much in front of him waiting to be grasped. And now he's dead.

Jack: I didn't want to die.

Rosie: And I wonder what God must make of all of this. Such senseless waste, such cruel loss. No reason, no point … just death. I can't help but believe God cries along with us. He must think we're mad.

Jack: And I heard the sound of the crows squawking in the morning mist.

Weep with those who weep

(Two angels are looking downwards)

Michael: Look at them down there, Gabriel.

Gabriel: I'm afraid I can hardly bring myself to look, Michael.

Michael: I know what you mean. I can't think what gets into their heads.

Gabriel: War, fighting, violence everywhere.

Michael: The things that we see every day – you'd think that, as angels, there would be something that we could do.

Gabriel: You know we're not allowed.

Michael: But how can God bear it?

Gabriel: He can't, he weeps every day as we do.

Michael: I saw a terrorist attack on a school bus yesterday – almost an entire group of schoolgirls wiped out, only one survivor.

Gabriel: What gets into their heads? What do they think they're going to achieve? What is going on in the mind of a person who can do that?

Michael: Do they have any sense at all of the pain and heartache they cause?

Gabriel: They can't do. Because if they'd seen the mothers' tears as we have, the broken hearts …

Michael: Then they wouldn't do it.

Gabriel: Exactly. How many wars have we seen, Michael?

Michael: I dread to think. I've watched torture, bloodshed, and people dying in the most horrible ways imaginable, innocent people caught up in the conflicts.

Gabriel: And what's it always about? Power, land, politics …

Michael: And, heaven help us … religion.

Gabriel: How dare they?

Michael: It's almost as if they'd never read the Bible.

Gabriel: Or the Koran, or any one of the sacred texts that they've got.

Michael: And, of course, the people who start the fighting ...

Gabriel: Are always the ones farthest behind the front line.

Michael: You'd think that after all these years they'd be tired of it. That after all the appalling examples they'd have realized by now that the only thing that results from war is misery.

Gabriel: But instead of that they just pour money and resources into inventing new and ever-more efficient and deadly ways of killing each other.

Michael: All of that God-given creativity and imagination squandered ...

Gabriel: What a heartbreaking waste.

Michael: It's a scandal, that's what is. How could they?

Gabriel: Didn't we tell them that Jesus was the Prince of Peace?

Michael: I distinctly remember taking the choir down there and singing about it.

Gabriel: Oh, that was a lovely night.

Michael: Sheep, shepherds, shocked expressions ... it was great.

Gabriel: They wrote it down too.

Michael: In the Bible ... I remember.

Gabriel: And it's not like most of them haven't got a copy of that on their bookshelf at home.

Michael: Some of them even read it.

Gabriel: So why don't they take notice of what it says then?

Michael: Who knows? It's almost as if they enjoy hating each other ...

Gabriel: And fighting.

Michael: Lives shattered.

Gabriel: Bodies broken.

Michael: While we sit.

Gabriel: And watch.

Michael: And weep with those who weep.

Gabriel: And stir the hearts of those who work for peace.

The correspondence

(A young man and woman sit at two writing desks a good distance apart)

Richard: *(reading as he writes)* Dear Anne, I have now been here a couple of days and have only now got time to sit and write to you. Life here on the front is very different from what I expected. The conditions are pretty grim. The constant stench in the trenches is terrible, and there are rats everywhere. I have made good friends with two other chaps, Charlie and Frank – both of them from Bristol – and we talk a lot about home. I think of you constantly and want nothing more than to return to you safely. Yours, Richard.

Anne: *(reading as she writes)* Dearest Richard, I have just received your letter. How wonderful it is to receive word from you. I cannot begin to imagine how terrible it must be for you. I am out of my mind with worry. I have tried to imagine what it must be like in the trenches but find I cannot. I am glad that there are people from home that you feel you can talk to. Please give my regards to Charlie and Frank. Promise that you will return to me. Mummy and Daddy send their regards. With love, Anne.

Richard: Dearest Anne, I am so sorry to have caused you worry – it was not my intention, but I did not feel that I could lie to you about how things are. Each day is the same. We are under constant bombardment from shells and rifle fire. There was an attempt at a small push forward two nights ago and eighteen people died. Grenades and machine-gun fire ripped through the group – not one of them was more than twenty-two years old. Most of them were teenagers. You will know that I have never been terribly religious but over the past few days I have taken to praying. I have never prayed much before so I am not sure quite what to say, what words to use. My prayers tend to be very simple. 'Please, Lord, help me' is one that I use. I also remember you and the rest of the family at home. My only problem is that as I look around myself at the carnage of war, I wonder whether God is here at all. You are always in my thoughts. With all my love, Richard.

Anne: My dearest Richard, I hardly know what to write to you. I cannot begin to imagine the things that you have seen and experienced. All I want to do is to see you again and hold you in my arms. I was so glad to hear that you have started praying. I am certain that God is there with you. I am not certain that you will always be able to feel his presence, or know that he is there, but I am convinced that he is. I sometimes wonder whether the only thing that God can do is to try to help us to get through the terrible things that we manage to do to each other. How can it be any other? When I think about this war – the violence and the bloodshed – I can only think of God weeping as I weep every night. I pray for the mothers and fathers, the families of those people who you saw die. The amount of grief that I see around me every day is terrible. People seem to be walking around in a daze, hardly able to think about what is happening. I can only pray that God will keep you safe and bring you back to me as soon as possible.

Richard: Dearest Anne, I hardly know where to start. Yesterday Frank was killed. He was hit by a sniper bullet and died in my arms. There is no happy ending, there is no sense. He leaves a wife and a three-year-old son back in Bristol. I thought I might write to them but I don't know what I would say. I prayed with him as he slipped away and at least he seemed to be at peace. I have to be honest with you and tell you that I do not know how much more of this I can stand. Your letters have meant so much to me and I am beginning to see God more clearly in the acts of love and humanity that I see around me in the midst of this chaos. I cannot believe that any of this is his will. Your letters mean more to me than I can ever tell you. Yours, Richard.

Anne: Dearest Richard, I received your letter yesterday, and this morning I got your telegram telling me that you are coming home on leave in three weeks' time. I cannot begin to tell you how excited, how joyful I am that you are coming home at last. I am not sure how God answers prayers, but this has certainly been at the centre of mine. At the moment I could not care less whether this was a selfish wish or not, I am so glad that you will be home again. This war has changed so much ... I know that. But I have to believe that at the centre of everything is God, and that his love for us, his will that we should live in love and peace with each other is at the heart of all that is. No matter what the war has done to each of us – that love will never fail us and it will enable us to cope with all that has taken place and find healing in the middle of it. I long to see you again and am counting the minutes. Yours for ever, Anne.

Effects

(An actor walks to the front)

Actor 1:   For the longest time I didn't believe ... couldn't believe that Jesus could care for somebody like me. That Jesus could love ... me. I knew what the theory was, I'd heard people tell me that he loved me, but I didn't believe it, *(pause)* I couldn't. I didn't find it at all surprising that Jesus could love the people who go to church, I mean, there's nothing not to love, is there? Well, yes, they're a bit self-righteous, a bit priggish at times, but they're good. They help each other. They help other people ... perhaps when it doesn't cost them too much but they *do* do it. I've never helped anybody, except myself. Nobody's ever been able to say, 'Steve – now he's a good bloke, my life is so much better because Steve's around.' I've been sat here for two and a half years, day in and day out – that's a lot of time. A lot of time to sit and think. It's not that I'm not sorry for what I've done. I am, more sorry than perhaps I can ever say. And perhaps it's because of that that I find it difficult to forgive myself, and therefore difficult to understand how anybody else could want to forgive me, how anybody else could love me. Let's be honest, I am not a loveable person, I'm not cute, I'm not sympathetic. I'm difficult, and people find it hard to cope with me. They don't know what to say. How do you start a conversation with somebody who's in prison? *(pause)* And yet I am told that Jesus loves me. Not for the person I could become but for who I am now. And that if I am sorry for what I've done, really sorry, and if I ask him to forgive me ... then he will. *(pause)* If that's true, then it's the best news I've ever heard.

(Another actor enters and sits – younger than the first and more aggressive)

Actor 2: I'm not even going to try and begin to tell you why I'm here, right? 'Cos then you'll judge me, I know how it goes. You'll want to know what I did, 'cos some crimes are worse than others, right, and you like to hear what a bad person I am ... how messed up I am. Well, I'm not going to give you the satisfaction. People have been judging me my whole life. Parents, teachers, social workers. And I know there's some people will say, 'Yeah, but some people overcome their backgrounds, right? Some people make the right choices.' Well I didn't, right? I didn't. I made some really bad choices. And I'm not blaming anybody else for that, right? I mean, yes, my parents were a mess and school wasn't much better. But *I* got into trouble. *I* made the choices that I made. I might have made different choices *now,* but there's not much point getting upset about that, is there? It's finished – over with. The problem is the future – 'cos I don't know what's going to happen. I mean, what do I do when I get out of here? How do I start again? What do I do about the temptation to go back to the way things were before? Because it'll be there ... I know it will. The temptation's always there. And I have to say the team here have been good, y'know. The Chaplain and the visitors. They've talked to me about how things were before. About what life was like. And I've told them – I've given them all the graphic detail. I think I did that because I wanted to see if they'd be shocked ... I mean, it was pretty bad. But give 'em their due, they weren't shocked. I suppose they've heard it all before. And they were sympathetic. And perhaps the most important thing – they've shown me care, they've listened to me – that's about the first time anybody's ever done that. They've loved me. No questions, no judgements, loved me for who I am. That doesn't mean they don't care if I go wrong. In fact, for the first time in my life I've actually got somebody who seems to care whether I make the right choices or not, and who's not going to shout at me if I go wrong. That means a lot. I've never had much time for church or religion – 'boring, not relevant' I used to say – but if the people here are anything to go by, there may be more to this Jesus stuff than meets the eye. Yeah, more than meets the eye.

Young people

(Two young people come to the front – at a push they could be played by adults)

One: I am a young person.

Two: *(pointing at One)* And I am an even younger person than he is.

One: We come to church every week.

Two: Well, most weeks anyway.

One: Regular as clockwork.

Two: And everybody says that they want us here.

One: Well, they certainly moan if we're not here.

Two: 'Where are the young people?' they say.

One: 'Where are the children?'

Two: 'We used to have lots of them.'

One: 'I blame the parents. They don't encourage them.'

Two: 'I blame football and car boot sales. There's too many distractions.'

One: 'I blame television. They just sit in front of the box.'

Two: Yes, everybody says that they want us here.

One: But does anybody shake us by the hand on the way out of church?

Two: Does anybody ask us what we think?

One: Does anybody ask us to do anything to help?

Two: Does anybody listen to us?

One: Even the older ones?

Two: Or are we a bit of a nuisance?

One: I think we are, you know.

Two: We are what?

One: A bit of a nuisance.

Two: Well, we want to get involved.

One: We want to do things, take part.

Two: We want to feel this church is ours.

One: We want people to listen to us.

Two: To express our ideas.

One: Perhaps even change one or two things.

Two: But certainly to be taken seriously.

One: And never, EVER be told ...

Two: 'You're only young, you don't understand these things.'

One: All of that ...

Two: Makes us a bit of a nuisance.

One: Sorry, we don't mean to be.

Two: But the problem is people don't want to take us seriously.

One: Because that would involve change.

Two: And that would never do.

One: No, that would never do.

Two: Sometimes we get the feeling ...

One: Only sometimes, mind you ...

Two: That some of you ...

One: Just some of you ...

Two: Don't like children very much.

One: Crazy, I know.

Two: So why are you surprised that most of our friends don't come with us?

One: Why do you assume it's our fault that there aren't more of us here?

Two: Or the fault of our parents?

One: Or television?

Two: Or car boot sales?

One: Or football?

Two: Of course, it can't be the church.

One: It's never the church.

Two: 'No,' you say, 'there must be something to blame.'

One: 'And it's certainly not us.'

Esther and Chris

(An older person stands centrally)

Esther: Good morning, everybody. You know, I've been teaching Sunday School a lot of years. More years than I care to remember. And there I go you see – calling it 'Sunday School' when it should be 'Junior Church'. And that's just one of the changes – which have been huge, by the way. But you know what? I still love it. I love it just as much as I did when I first started. I love to see the expression on a child's face when they hear a story for the first time. I love the wide-eyed wonder of it all. I love … *(during this a child has come on from behind her and tugs at her sleeve)*

Chris: Excuse me … I've got a question.

Esther: Oh, hello Chris. Yes … what's the question?

Chris: Well … there's not just one question.

Esther: Oh? Well, just how many are there?

Chris: About a million and six.

Esther: Gracious … that's a lot of questions. Why don't you start with the first one and go on from there?

Chris: Okay. Why did my hamster have to die and will I see him in heaven? Does God really hear my prayer when there must be millions of prayers to listen to? Why are people so horrible to each other all the time? Why does my little brother get on my nerves so much? Why do people in church look so miserable all the time – I thought we were meant to be happy?

Esther: Okay, I think you can stop now.

Chris: But I've still got more questions.

Esther: I know you have. But is it all right if I ask *you* a question?

Chris: Yeah, I s'pose.

Esther: Is it going to be okay with you if not all of your questions have answers?

Chris: But I thought you knew everything?

Esther: Whatever gave you that idea? I just look like I know everything, that's all. It's just that the answer to some of your questions is 'I don't know.'

Chris: Well, that's not a very good answer.

Esther: Actually, it's not a bad one. At least it's honest, and you wouldn't want me to tell fibs, would you?

Chris: No.

Esther: There you go, you see. I'm not sure about your hamster, Chris, and I wish people could be kinder to each other and that Christians would look a little happier. But I do know one thing that kind of answers all the others.

Chris: And what's that?

Esther: I don't know all that much but I do know the one thing that I *need* to know. It's more important than all the other things that I'll ever tell you, it's more important than all the things you'll ever learn in school.

Chris: What is it?

Esther: The creator of the entire universe, with all of its stars and galaxies and planets, the maker of all of that, who we call God, loves *you.* And there is nothing that you can do or say and nowhere that you can go that will ever stop God from loving you.

Chris: Does God love everybody?

Esther: Absolutely everybody.

Chris: Even my uncle Steve?

Esther: Even your uncle Steve. And our job is to try and spread that love.

Chris: Spread it?

Esther: Yes – show it to other people. Do loving things for others and slowly, bit by bit, you change them and change the world. And most importantly – by showing love we show God's glory. We help people to see what God is like.

Chris: But I don't even like my little brother – how am I meant to be loving to other people?

Esther: Sometimes showing love to the people we're closest to is the hardest bit. But don't worry ... ask God and he'll help you even to love your little brother.

Chris: That would be a miracle.

Esther: It certainly would.

Chris: Okay – I'll go and try it. Thanks. 'Bye. (exits)

Esther: And that's why I love this work so much. I love the questions and the enthusiasm and the frustration and the joy – but most of all I just love them. (she smiles to herself and exits)

Kirsty and Hayley on young people

(Two actors stand at the front)

Kirsty: So I was telling Chantrelle that, like, I've got to go to church on Sunday.

Hayley: You've got to go where, Kirsty?

Kirsty: Church. An', like, it's dead scary, right, 'cos, like, my little nephew is getting christened, right, an' he's, like, a little monster.

Hayley: Oh, I've seen him. He's what, like, eighteen months old an' they're gellin' his hair already an' he's got an ear piercing done.

Kirsty: That's the one, Hayley. An', like, Sunday morning's the only day I get a lie-in, right, but my mum's all, like, 'You're going to let down the family if you don't come.' Like I care.

Hayley: So what do they do in church?

Kirsty: How should I know, it's, like, full of dead old people. I was goin' to take my iPod, then I could listen to music.

Hayley: But don't they have music in church?

Kirsty: Yeah, but, right, it's all either dead old hymns or a guy in corduroy trousers playin' a guitar.

Hayley: I s'pose you're right.

Kirsty: I know I'm right, and it's all going to be getting up and sitting down and, like, not knowing what you've got to do when, an' followin' words out of some dead smelly book.

Hayley: An' full of people with no taste in clothes.

Kirsty: Oh, it's goin' to be 'orrible, an' there's goin' to be mum giving me really evil glares the whole time.

Hayley: What if I was to come with you, Kirsty?

Kirsty: You, like, come to church, with me?

Hayley: Yeah.

Kirsty: Like, you'd do something like that for me?

Hayley: Like, 'course. It would be a laugh.

Kirsty: Oh ... I'm all choked up, that's, like, the nicest thing anybody's ever done for me.

Hayley: It'll be all right, an' then after the service we can tell the vicar what's what, right?

Kirsty: Oh yeah, that'll be like cool, right, 'cos the church is always saying that they want to know what the youth think.

Hayley: Well, they'd need a new building, right, 'cos, like, stonework is *so* last year.

Kirsty: Yeah, like, they need electric pink everywhere.

Hayley: An' a dead good-lookin' vicar who's, like, eighteen years old, right?

Kirsty: An' wears dead trendy clothes.

Hayley: They'd have to have, like, new music, right?

Kirsty: Yeah, an' make it REALLY loud.

Hayley: An' they could have a laser light show, an', like, strobes an' all that.

Kirsty: An', like, a bar, right, that gives free drinks away.

Hayley: Now that'd be a church I'd go to.

Kirsty: Me too.

Hayley: Uh, Kirsty?

Kirsty: Yeah, Hayley?

Hayley: What's church actually there to do?

Kirsty: Whadya mean?

Hayley: Well, like, there's all these church buildings around, right? What do they do?

Kirsty: My mum says it's, like, something to do with Jesus, an' worship, an' the meaning of life.

Hayley: Oh ... so us turning it into a nightclub might not work.

Kirsty: Oh, I'd never thought of that.

Hayley: No ... perhaps, like, we ought to think about our ideal church a little bit harder.

Kirsty: My thinking just makes my brain hurt.

Hayley: You're right. Let's watch *EastEnders* instead.

Kirsty: Brilliant idea, 'cos, like, there's no thinking involved there at all.

Hayley: You're right there.

Yes, Prime Minister

(The Prime Minister walks on, Geoffrey follows on)

Geoffrey:	Good morning, Prime Minister.
PM:	Good morning, Geoffrey. How are we today?
Geoffrey:	As always, sir, we are outstanding.
PM:	You see, Geoffrey, that's why you're my favourite advisor. Everything should always be outstanding.
Geoffrey:	Indeed, sir.
PM:	So, what's on the list for today, then?
Geoffrey:	Well, you've got a speech to investment bankers in the City at 10.30 a.m.
PM:	Excellent.
Geoffrey:	Then there's an interview on the *World at One* at lunchtime.
PM:	Jolly good.
Geoffrey:	Then you're seeing the ambassador from Zambia at 3 o'clock.
PM:	Oh dear.
Geoffrey:	Oh dear?
PM:	Yes indeed, oh dear.
Geoffrey:	Is something wrong, Prime Minister?
PM:	Well, it's just that if the ambassador of Zambia is coming I know just what he's going to want to talk about.
Geoffrey:	And what's that, Prime Minister?
PM:	AIDS.
Geoffrey:	Well, isn't that an important thing to be able to talk about?
PM:	Oh, absolutely it is, Geoffrey. HIV, AIDS is a vital issue. Far more so for the people of Zambia than for the people of Britain.

Geoffrey: Quite right, Prime Minister. It's dreadful. Do you know there are thousands upon thousands of AIDS orphans now? Some estimates put the number as high as one in ten children.

PM: As I said, Geoffrey, I quite understand the issue, and it's an important one and I'd love to be able to do more about it.

Geoffrey: This sounds as though there's going to be a 'but' in the sentence somewhere.

PM: But the electorate here just wouldn't wear it. The problem is thousands of miles away in somebody else's backyard, and it seems huge and unsolvable and most important of all …

Geoffrey: Yes, Prime Minister?

PM: It doesn't lend itself to coverage on the TV news.

Geoffrey: It doesn't?

PM: Of course not. The issue has already gone on for years and it's going to go on for years to come. TV news likes stories that are going to be over in a week or two. Also – showing teenagers dying of AIDS is not a good thing to put on the 6 o'clock news. You'd have to warn people that they might find the report distressing and then people would just change channels.

Geoffrey: So we're not going to do anything, then?

PM: I didn't say that – we're just not going to do as much as we could. We'll leave it to other organizations who don't have to win elections. The charity sector does loads, Christian Aid, Oxfam, CAFOD.

Geoffrey: They've hardly got the resources that we have.

PM: Well, we'll do our bit. It just won't be an easy sell.

Geoffrey: So what do I tell the ambassador?

PM: Tell him I'll see him at 3 p.m., but that there are some issues that aren't to be discussed.

Candles

(Two actors stand centrally)

Actor 1: You know what, Rodney?

Actor 2: What's that then, Pamela?

Actor 1: I hate this time of year.

Actor 2: So do I – with a vengeance.

Actor 1: I mean, everybody's full of festive cheer.

Actor 2: Peace and goodwill to all.

Actor 1: But when you're a candle ...

Actor 2: Yes, when you're a candle ...

Actor 1: It's miserable ...

Actor 2: Depressing.

Actor 1: The only thing worse would be if you were a turkey.

Actor 2: Yeah, I don't suppose they're looking forward to Christmas either.

Actor 1: But being a candle is such a pain at Christmas.

Actor 2: Particularly when you're small candles like us.

Actor 1: I mean, if you were a big chunky, slow-burning candle ...

Actor 2: Then they'd put you out the front and you'd be there for all to see.

Actor 1: If you were a mid-sized candle ...

Actor 2: You might get put in the Advent Ring.

Actor 1: That would be nice. And if you were one of those huge novelty candles with three wicks that looked like a train ...

Actor 2: The chances are you'd never get lit at all.

Actor 1: Nah – you'd just get stuck on a mantelpiece 'cos nobody's sure which wick to light first, or how you're going to burn.

Actor 2: Or they say, 'Oooh what a lovely novelty candle, it seems a shame to light it, let's put it over here on the bookcase instead.'

Actor 1: But no, when you're a small candle like us ...

Actor 2: The chances are that the cruellest torture of all awaits you.

Actor 1: Yes, the likelihood is they're going to do the worst thing that they can do to any candle.

Actor 2: A fate worse than death.

Actor 1: They're going to put you into ... a Christingle.

Actor 2: Oh, the shame! All that orange juice squirting round your bottom.

Actor 1: All those cocktail sticks with huge amounts of sweets on them.

Actor 2: They light you for about a minute.

Actor 1: And then they blow you out ...

Actor 2: And stuff themselves with the sweets.

Actor 1: Of course, as soon as you've been blown out and the sweets have been eaten, what use are you?

Actor 2: What use are you?

Actor 1: None at all.

Actor 2: The interest has completely disappeared.

Actor 1: After all, who wants to eat an orange with candle wax on it?

Actor 2: So we get thrown away.

Actor 1: Tossed aside like an old boot!

Actor 2: Oh, the indignity of it all.

Actor 1: Oh, the shame.

Actor 2: So that is our fate this year.

Actor 1: Miserable, isn't it?

Actor 2: *(leans forward and listens)* Wait a minute, did you hear that?

Actor 1: What?

Actor 2: The preacher ... he just mentioned us.

Actor 1: *(excited)* Did he? What did he say?

Actor 2: He said we're the most important part of the whole Christingle.

Actor 1:   Important? Us? How?

Actor 2:   He said that we represent Jesus – who came as a light into a very dark world.

Actor 1:   So we *are* important. I knew it!

Actor 2:   So no matter how dark the world becomes ...

Actor 1:   And however lonely and hopeless it sometimes seems ...

Actor 2:   A light always shines.

Actor 1:   And the darkness cannot put it out.

Actor 2:   So let your light shine.

Actor 1:   Just like ours!

The marketing meeting

(Two actors stand with a flip chart or large graph)

Jess: So then, Les, what have we got?

Les: Well, Jess, as you know our focus groups have been telling us that they think Christmas has become too commercialized. They're sick of seeing stockings and cards in the shops in August, they're tired of hearing carols from early November – they want something new, something that speaks of the real spirit of Christmas. Something that makes them feel good about themselves.

Jess: And that's just what we're going to give them ... at a price of course. So, you've been looking at what Christians do around Christmas to see how we can make some money out of it. Is that right?

Les: Absolutely.

Jess: Tell me again, why Christians?

Les: Well, it's because it's *their* festival.

Jess: It is? Well, you learn something new every day on this job.

Les: Anyway, after extensive research I've come up with the perfect product. It takes a favourite traditional symbol of Christmas and it tweaks it just a little so we can make large amounts of dosh on it.

Jess: And this symbol is?

Les: Right here *(takes out Christingle)*. It's called a CHRIS ... tingle.

Jess: *(looking at it)* So what does it do?

Les: Well, our research tells us you light the candle and then you eat the sweets.

Jess: Is that it?

Les: Well, there's something about the candle representing the light of the world or something.

Jess: What about the red ribbon?

Les: Well, apparently that's about the blood of Jesus.

Jess: Eurgh! We're going to have to lose that. What on earth do these Christians think they're doing? Blood at Christmas? Who wants that?

Les: I know ... weird, isn't it?

Jess: Okay, here's what I'm thinking. First we lose the fruit.

Les: What, the orange?

Jess: Absolutely. They're messy and smelly and the most important thing is that the profit margin is awful. We replace it with a plastic orange which splits in the middle and has a little plastic toy inside. Missiles and tanks for the boys, little dolly things with bad hair for the girls.

Les: That's a great idea.

Jess: We lose the red ribbon and replace it with a tattoo glitter strip that you can peel off the plastic orange and attach round your wrist as a fashion accessory. How cool is that?

Les: You're a genius. What about the sweets? They're meant to represent the fruits of the Spirit or something like that.

Jess: Perfect, with talk of spirits we can launch it at Hallowe'en. But this candle has got to go. Naked flame ... I mean, think of all the lawsuits.

Les: Nightmare. What about a funky little glow-strip thing. One of those that you snap and it glows fluorescent for an hour or so.

Jess: Great. Oh, this is so much better than what the Christians have. Sweets, a toy, fashion accessories and a glow-strip.

Les: What would it retail for?

Jess: Well, we can source all the materials for about 50p.

Les: So I'm thinking £5.99.

Jess: Oh, at least. It'll be the new must-have toy of the Christmas season.

Les: Every parent will have to buy one for their kiddies' stockings.

Jess: We can market it as being retro cool so the teenagers will think they've got to have one as well.

Les: We're onto a goldmine here.

Jess: And the best thing is it's all about the true spirit of Christmas.

Les: Oh, absolutely. We've left the spirit of the thing completely intact. Cash registers here we come!

Robert and Katy on Christingles

(Robert and Katy are seven-year-olds played by adults)

Robert: *(very excited)* Can't wait, can't wait, can't wait!

Katy: *(entering)* What are you so excited about, then?

Robert: Only the best church service of the whole year.

Katy: What d'ya mean?

Robert: Well, like, most church services are really boring, aren't they? It's all talk, talk, talk, be a better person, do this, don't do that, yack, yack, yack.

Katy: So what's so different this week then?

Robert: Don't you know nothing? This week's the Christingle service.

Katy: Ah, cool.

Robert: Exactly … cool. The only service of the year when I get to play with a naked flame!

Katy: Last year you nearly set fire to Pamela Smeakley's coat.

Robert: *(remembering)* Oh yeah … that was great.

Katy: Except for the fact that your Dad stopped sweet privileges for a whole three days.

Robert: *(suddenly serious)* That was the longest three days of my life.

Katy: Do we get to make our Christingles at home again this year?

Robert: I think so. Dad said the grown-ups at church were tired of getting the juice from a hundred and twenty oranges sprayed over their hands.

Katy: That's better, 'cos that means we get to put our own sweets on. When they make them at church they're really mingy sweet-wise.

Robert: And *we* can pile them REALLY high.

Katy: Last year you couldn't see my orange for the sweets.

Robert: My Christingle had twenty-seven sweets on … I counted.

Katy: Well, mine had a … a zillion and six on.

Robert: That's impossible.

Katy: No it isn't ... I counted them.

Robert: Anyway – what with the sweets and the naked flame – that makes Christingle my favourite service of the whole year.

Katy: And it's all about Jesus.

Robert: Is it?

Katy: Of course it is. Honestly, you're so dim sometimes.

Robert: Well how is it about Jesus then?

Katy: Well, the orange is the world.

Robert: But the world isn't orange ... it's blue and green and things ... I've seen a photo.

Katy: Well, it's not *actually* the world is it? It's a symbol.

Robert: Isn't that a thing that makes a great crashing sound when you play it?

Katy: Yeah, I think so.

Robert: So how come the world's like that then?

Katy: I don't know – it's adult stuff. *(carrying on)* The candle is the light of Jesus.

Robert: Even when it sets light to Pamela Smeakley's coat?

Katy: No, that's just you being you. Then the red ribbon is for the blood of Jesus.

Robert: Going all round the world.

Katy: Exactly, and the sweets are ...

Robert: The sweets are for me.

Katy: I know that, but they stand for something.

Robert: Who cares? They're for me.

Katy: Now, is it the four corners of the world? Or the fruits of the earth, or the fruits of the Spirit?

Robert: Can't it be all of them as long as I get to eat them?

Katy: I suppose so.

Robert: Cool.

Katy: My mum says that the most important part of Christingle is to remember what it stands for.

Robert: My dad says it's a message that you hold in your hand.

Katy: I think our parents are quite clever really.

Robert: Absolutely. And when we sing the carol with all the candles glowing it's really pretty.

Katy: I think that's why it's my favourite service of the whole year.

Robert: And there's the sweets.

Katy: Oh yes – there's always the sweets.